Thinking by numbers

Written by *PAUL BROADBENT*

Series editor STEVE HIGGINS

OXFORD
UNIVERSITY PRESS

OXFORD
UNIVERSITY PRESS

Great Clarendon Street, Oxford OX2 6DP

Oxford University Press is a department of the University of Oxford.
It furthers the University's objective of excellence in research,
scholarship, and education by publishing worldwide in

Oxford   New York

Auckland   Cape Town   Dar es Salaam   Hong Kong   Karachi
Kuala Lumpur   Madrid   Melbourne   Mexico City   Nairobi
New Delhi   Shanghai   Taipei   Toronto

With offices in

Argentina   Austria   Brazil   Chile   Czech Republic   France   Greece
Guatemala   Hungary   Italy   Japan   South Korea   Poland   Portugal
Singapore   Switzerland   Thailand   Turkey   Ukraine   Vietnam

Oxford is a registered trade mark of Oxford University Press
in the UK and in certain other countries

British Library Cataloguing in Publication Data

Data available

ISBN-13: 9780198361282
ISBN-10: 0 19 836128 9

3 5 7 9 10 8 6 4 2

Illustrated by Simon Smith
Typeset in Great Britain by Artistix, Thame, Oxon
Printed in Great Britain by Ashford Colour Press, Gosport, Hants

CR
SIO
THI

Contents

Introduction

Thinking by Numbers aims to develop thinking skills through mathematics lessons and activities across the primary age range. Although it can be used by an individual teacher, we think that you will get the best from the series if you use the activities across your school to undertake a professional inquiry into the potential of these lessons to develop pupils' thinking. Hence, the sections on *Professional development* (page 9), *Classroom management* (page 12), *Formative assessment and assessment for learning* (page 14), and *Speaking and listening* (page 18) are important aspects of the series. These sections will support you in helping to make the activities successful, as well as suggesting opportunities to develop aspects of your own teaching. Most of these introductory sections also contain suggestions for further reading that will support your exploration of thinking skills through the activities in *Thinking by Numbers*.

Teaching children to think for themselves is at the heart of primary education. It is all too easy to focus on the demands of the curriculum and its assessment and forget that the facts and knowledge have to be connected with an understanding of this curriculum content to help the learner make sense of it all. Without this understanding learners cannot use the information they have been taught and see how it relates to other ideas or knowledge that they have already. At the core of the thinking skills movement in education is the belief that this kind of thinking is teachable. This belief has been inspired by the work of two leading educators.

History of thinking skills

In Israel after the Second World War, many refugee children had been through traumatic early experiences. On traditional tests, such as IQ tests or standardized tests of achievement, many of these children scored so badly that they seemed 'unteachable'. Working to integrate such children Reuven Feuerstein refused to accept this conclusion and devised ways to find out exactly which kinds of thinking they were unable to do, how they could be helped to develop these skills, and, therefore, each individual's *potential* for learning.

Feuerstein developed a set of techniques and tasks called 'instruments' that helped these learners succeed on subsequent tests. These methods were termed 'dynamic', in the sense that children were studying the process of learning and the change that took place. Feuerstein argued that such a process was much more likely to predict how a person might then learn in the future. Many of Feuerstein's ideas have influenced work on teaching thinking skills, in particular his emphasis on the importance of the interaction of the teacher, or 'mediation' of thinking.

Another important figure in thinking skills (or 'Critical Thinking', as it is called in the United States), is the American philosopher Matthew Lipman. As a university professor, he thought that his students had been encouraged to learn facts and to accept opinions, but not to think for themselves. He developed a programme, therefore, called 'Philosophy for Children', which aims to help younger people (from six-year-olds to teenagers) to think by raising questions about stories that they read together. The teacher uses children's natural curiosity about the stories in order to promote active participation and learning. One of Lipman's basic convictions is that children are natural philosophers, and that they view the world around them with curiosity and wonder, which can be used as a basis for thinking and reasoning.

Both Feuerstein and Lipman, though from very different starting-points, hold a similar belief in children's abilities. They have demonstrated that through thinking exercises and activities learners can exceed the predictions of achievement which tests may have suggested is their limit of competence. This, then, forms the basis of techniques in thinking skills – realizing children's potential. Their work has inspired many others to explore and develop approaches which help children to become more effective learners as they start to think for themselves. The aim of this book is to help you, as a teacher, to see how this kind of thinking can be developed.

Teaching thinking

Some people argue that the idea of trying to teach general thinking skills is misguided because in practice thinking always occurs in a specific situation. Further, they believe that it is better to concentrate on teaching subjects and developing specific and detailed knowledge. However, *Thinking by Numbers* has been developed on the principle that there are common features of thinking in different situations, that it is helpful to try to apply techniques learned previously in new situations. For example, once you have used a graphic organizer, such as a Venn diagram, to compare and contrast themes in traditional tales in literacy, you can use the same technique to compare and contrast in other curriculum areas, such as family life in different eras in history.

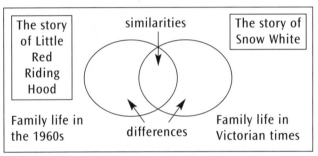

Since 1999, the national curricula for England and Wales now specifically include thinking skills (see page 6 for more details). In Scotland the *5–14 Guidelines* emphasize the capacity for independent thought through enquiry, problem solving, information handling and reasoning, as well as identifying learning and thinking skills in the core skills and capabilities. So the current challenge for teachers is not whether to teach thinking skills, but how best to teach them!

Approaches to teaching thinking skills

There is a host of different programmes and approaches which advocate teaching thinking. These can be categorized broadly into whether they adopt an 'enrichment' approach where they are taught through extra or separate lessons, or an 'infusion' approach where the particular skills are taught through the normal lessons that schools provide. There are certain advantages and

disadvantages to adopting these two different teaching approaches. If thinking skills are taught separately it is possible to make skills and techniques explicit, but there is a danger that they may not be used, except in special 'thinking' lessons. However, if they are taught as part of other lessons, such as mathematics or history, there is also a danger that the skills and techniques will become submerged by the curriculum content and not be seen as skills that can be applied elsewhere.

We believe that it is necessary to do both – to have a mixture of 'thinking lessons' with discussion of the kinds of thinking that are involved, and 'subject lessons' where skills can be applied and developed, but perhaps less explicitly. Identifying some lessons as 'thinking maths' lessons gives a clear signal to the children that you are looking for something different in the way that they work and the way they talk and listen. It is challenging to make the time to develop speculation or reasoning in every lesson, but it is also difficult to make sure it happens at *some* time in *some* lessons. We suggest that the activities in the different units can be used as a way to emphasize aspects of thinking that you wish to develop. You may then choose to develop other similar lessons where you can re-use the structure of the activities, or use some of the ideas and techniques in other subject areas.

Suggestions for further reading
H. Sharron and M. Coulter, *Changing Children's Minds: Feuerstein's Revolution in the teaching of Intelligence* (Birmingham, Questions Publishing Company, 1994)

M. Lipman, *Thinking in Education* (Cambridge University Press, 2003)

C. McGuinness, *From thinking skills to thinking classrooms: A review and evaluation of approaches for developing pupils' thinking* [DfEE Research Report RR115] (Norwich, HMSO, 1999)

V. Wilson, *Can Thinking Skills Be Taught? A paper for discussion* (Edinburgh, Scottish Council for Research in Education, 2000) [Available at: http://www.scre.ac.uk/scot-research/thinking/index.html]

Thinking skills and the National Curriculum

Classifying thinking skills

There are more ways to think about thinking than you could imagine! Amongst the wealth of lists, frameworks, models and taxonomies of thinking that have been developed, many people have heard of the 'Bloom's Taxonomy', which is considered the original way of classifying 'higher order thinking'. This taxonomy is basically a three-tier model:

- **knowledge** – in the form of facts, concepts, rules or skills
- **basic thinking** – relatively simple ways of understanding, elaborating and using what is known
- **higher order thinking** – a learning process which leads to a deeper understanding of the nature, justification, implications and value of what is known.

The National Curriculum in England uses five classification headings to denote thinking skills that should be embedded across all subject areas so pupils learn how to learn. These are:

- evaluation
- creativity
- enquiry
- reasoning
- information processing.

However, no single classification or framework can ever fully describe the complexity of all the kinds of thinking we experience. What is missing in both the original version of Bloom's work and in the National Curriculum list is the role of the thinker in thinking – one's own awareness, reflection and engagement. This metacognitive component (i.e. thinking about how we think) is an essential ingredient in developing a learner's understanding of their own thinking and the ability to think for oneself. The following table shows how *Thinking by Numbers* works alongside these thinking classifications to develop thinking skills.

Bloom's Taxonomy	National Curriculum	Thinking by Numbers	
Knowledge Abstracts and universals Using specifics Knowledge of specifics	*Information processing*	Unit 1: Sort it out!	*Unit 6: Think on!*
Basic thinking Application Comprehension			
Higher order thinking Evaluation Synthesis Analysis	*Reasoning* *Enquiry* *Creativity* *Evaluation*	Unit 2: That's because … Unit 3: Detective work Unit 4: What if? Unit 5: In my opinion	

Comparison of Bloom's Taxonomy, the National Curriculum and *Thinking by Numbers*

The National Curriculum

The National Curriculum categories contain the following breakdown of skills, which form the basis for the units in the *Thinking by Numbers* series.

Information processing skills

These enable pupils to locate and collect relevant information, to sort, classify, sequence, compare and contrast, and to analyse part/whole relationships.

Reasoning skills

These enable pupils to give reasons for opinions and actions, to draw inferences and make deductions, to use precise language to explain what they think, and to make judgements and decisions informed by reasons or evidence.

Enquiry skills

These enable pupils to ask relevant questions, to pose and define problems, to plan what to do and how to research, to predict outcomes and anticipate consequences, and to test conclusions and improve ideas.

Creative thinking skills

These enable pupils to generate and extend ideas, to suggest hypotheses, to apply imagination, and to look for alternative innovative outcomes.

Evaluation skills

These enable pupils to evaluate information, to judge the value of what they read, hear and do, to develop criteria for judging the value of their own and others' work or ideas, and to have confidence in their judgements.

The first five units of the *Thinking by Numbers* books are based on these classifications. We have also added two further components:

- ◗ a final unit which provides opportunities for **using and applying thinking skills** covered in the earlier units
- ◗ a **metacognitive skills** element running throughout all of the activities, which aims to develop children's awareness and understanding of the thinking they are doing.

Suggestions for further reading
L.W. Anderson and D.R. Krathwohl (eds.), *A Taxonomy for Learning, Teaching and Assessing: A revision of Bloom's Taxonomy of Educational Objectives* (New York, Longman, 2001)

S. Higgins, J. Miller, D. Moseley and J. Elliot, 'Taxonomy Heaven', *Teaching Thinking, 12*, (Autumn 2003)

Thinking skills in mathematics

Mathematics is an area of the curriculum which is full of opportunities to develop pupils' thinking skills and reasoning abilities. An emphasis on developing strategies, identifying patterns and rules, and clarifying concepts helps children learn mathematics by making aspects of it more explicit in the classroom. Developing reasoning, problem solving and enquiry skills through mathematics can support the development of these 'higher order' thinking skills more widely, and encourage successful learning in other subjects. A number of principles underpin the activities in each of the six units in *Thinking by Numbers*. These will help pupils to see the connections between the way that they have worked on a mathematics task and then how they can apply these skills in other contexts, either in other areas of mathematics or other areas of learning and understanding.

Challenge

Thinking activities must provide a level of challenge. This means that they should not be too easy to complete, nor so hard that the pupils cannot recognize that they have been successful. Alternatively, the activities may have more than one solution, or route to a solution, that can be evaluated by the pupils to decide which is the best answer or approach. Mathematics is a subject which people often think they just 'can't do'. Successfully completing challenges encourages pupils to see that maths is a subject that they can learn to be good at.

Active discussion

Thinking activities need to be talked about. Mathematics has both a vocabulary and a language of its own. Familiar words are used in unfamiliar ways, such as 'product' or 'difference', and it has its own terminology, such as 'numerator' or 'perpendicular'. Pupils will need time to practise speaking mathematically and explain what they are thinking using this language. This can be difficult to do with the whole class, so some paired or small group work is essential to provide opportunities to explore ideas and allow pupils to develop confidence with the vocabulary.

Feedback

Giving feedback will be key in ensuring pupils make progress in a thinking activity. One of the easiest ways to do this is to have 'mini-plenaries' as the lesson develops. Stop the class for a few minutes and ask a group to explain where they are up to. This will give you the chance to highlight successful ways of working, as well as asking for reasons and challenging their thinking.

Review

When developing thinking skills it is important to review both the **content** of the activity and the **process** that the pupils have used to complete the activity. This means talking about the mathematics involved in the task and the way that they have worked (the skills used in collaborating, working systematically, or identifying patterns and rules). It is often helpful to discuss the latter the next time pupils undertake a similar task so that you can remind them of what was successful. A combination of 'mini-plenaries' throughout the lesson, a review at the end of a lesson, then recapping at the beginning of the next lesson will help ensure children understand that you want them to think not just about *what* they have learned, but *how* they have learned it.

Professional development

We advocate that you try out the *Thinking by Numbers* activities as part of your professional development programme. A critical perspective on the lesson is essential. The activities alone will not succeed in developing thinking skills without this perspective. It is helpful to have a colleague with whom to discuss the activities as you try out the different ideas. We believe that a key part of teaching thinking and thinking skills successfully is to have some time and space to reflect on your own teaching so as to increase the emphasis on developing pupils' understanding. The introductory 'brief' and final 'debrief' sections of each activity aim to support this by summarizing the key features of the lessons and indicating aspects for review.

Thinking by Numbers provides a combination of teacher-led activities, then discussion and collaborative working in small groups, followed by some kind of whole class discussion, or plenary, which reviews both the content and process of learning. The results of this approach are usually a higher level of engagement in the activities, more talking and discussion about the activities. The activities themselves are open-ended to the extent that genuine discussion is not only possible but helpful. They are also challenging but enjoyable activities, helping to create a classroom climate where there is an emphasis on succeeding after effort.

As part of this process you should get more opportunities to hear what your pupils think. As you plan these lessons to increase engagement in learning you will need to listen carefully to how your pupils respond. The enjoyment should initially help to sustain more permanent changes in patterns of classroom interaction. The further feedback you get from insights into pupils' understanding will help identify any misunderstanding or misconceptions that you can tackle through 'mediation' or questioning and discussion.

Some suggestions for getting started:

1 **Work with a colleague**. This might be a colleague teaching the same year group, in which case you can investigate the impact of the same activities. Alternatively you may be working with a colleague in another year group, so you might look at similar kinds of activities or similar aspects of thinking. Working with a colleague means you are more likely to keep to your plan, building progress in time for review. Discussing things with someone else helps to clarify our own thinking, and makes it easier to see patterns or themes in what has happened.

2 **Decide what you want to investigate or improve**. It is easier to develop children's thinking if you focus on a particular area that you feel needs improvement. You could:
   - identify information processing as a key mathematical skill needing improvement
   - focus on your own questioning and how you probe and challenge your children's thinking
   - develop more precise use of mathematical language
   - aim to increase participation in lessons by children who are not usually engaged.

3 **Set a timescale** (at least eight weeks, up to a school year) and plan which activities you are going to use. How often will you have *Thinking by Numbers* lessons? Once a week? Once a fortnight? How will you make sure you have time to review the activities with a colleague?

4 **Try out the activities and review** them as soon afterwards as you can with your colleague. What was different in the lesson compared with other maths lessons? Were you able to see patterns in the children's thinking? Were there any common misconceptions that you needed to tackle? How well did the collaborative tasks go?

5 **Analyse what happened**. If there is improvement, what do you think caused it? The focused practice? Your extra time and effort? The pupils' discussion? Your understanding of their thinking? Would it probably have happened anyway?

6 **Review progress**. What have you learned that you can apply in the longer term? Do some kinds of questions work better than others? Can you use any of the strategies more widely?

How to use *Thinking by Numbers*

The activities in *Thinking by Numbers* can be used in different ways – there is no need to work through them in order, though the final unit is designed to let pupils apply the skills that they have developed. Therefore, for you to assess how well these skills have been learned, it should be used after some of the other activities in the first five units. Some of the activities are based on thinking skills strategies which can be used more widely either in mathematics or other subjects of the curriculum. You should therefore evaluate if there are any aspects of the activity or teaching technique which could be used more generally. Although the books are aimed at different age groups, you may find activities that you can use or adapt in other books in the series. This is particularly true of the generic strategies, such as 'odd one out', which can be used again in mathematics or other areas of the curriculum. See page 24 for a fuller description of some generic activities used throughout the series.

Just as enquiry is at the heart of thinking skills activities for pupils, we believe that it also needs to be a part of the way you use them as a teacher. None of the activities will work by themselves, and they will not all be equally effective since this depends on the existing skills and knowledge of your pupils. You will have to use them critically to see how they can help your pupils' thinking – it is impossible to do this directly, since we cannot see into our pupils' heads and know what they are thinking. Nevertheless, it is possible to plan a series of activities that enable you to find out about pupils' thinking at different times and in different ways. This allows you to infer their level of understanding. Therefore, this needs to be a process of enquiry – finding out what and how your pupils think. The 'Watch out for' and 'Listen for' sections of each activity should help with this process.

The units

The units are based around the classification of thinking skills in the National Curriculum for England and the headings of **information processing**, **reasoning**, **enquiry**, **creative thinking** and **evaluation**. Each unit begins with an overview of these particular aspects of thinking, and ends with a summary looking at how these skills can be developed. Of course, it is not possible to separate the thinking in different activities so that they only involve reasoning or creative thinking. Thinking is a complex activity which involves all kinds of thinking at the same time. It is holistic, multi-dimensional and dependent upon the context that we find ourselves in. The purpose of the tasks in *Thinking by Numbers* is to enable you to focus on a particular kind of thinking and to consider how it can be developed or fostered in your pupils.

Links

The appendices (pages 88 to 95) contain information about how *Thinking by Numbers* relates to the *Framework for Teaching Mathematics* used in England, and the *5–14 Guidelines* for Scotland. A glossary of thinking skills terms is also included on page 96 for reference.

Suggestions for further reading
P. Adey, *The Professional Development of Teachers: Practice and Theory* (Dordrecht, Kluwer Wolters, 2004)

S. Higgins, *Thinking Through Primary Teaching* (Cambridge, Chris Kington Publishing, 2001)

The activities

4 Each activity has a whole class introduction where you will be 'Setting the scene' and modelling the problem to the children.

1 Each activity has an introduction, 'The Brief', and review points, 'The Debrief', to explain the context for the activity. This is the 'professional development' part to help you consider what you want to achieve in the thinking lesson, and later to review how well it achieved its thinking skills aims.

6 The 'Checkpoints' section gives ideas for how to the keep the activity on track. This section also has suggestions on what to watch and listen out for, and prompts and pointers to stimulate discussion.

Day trip to the beach

BRIEF

'Day trip to the beach' is an open-ended problem-solving task, involving decision-making by the children in pairs. Review some of the earlier activities that they have done and explain that this task is a chance for them to use these skills. They should use the information presented on the sheets to inform their judgements and help them work out a good day on the beach for two children, Dan and Lucy. The information shows times and prices for different items and events, presented as a series of posters and notices. The children need to organize and evaluate this information, assimilating it as a time line for Dan and Lucy's day.

Key maths links
- Making decisions
- Problems involving time and money

Thinking skills
- Solving problems
- Evaluating information
- Making judgements and decisions informed by evidence

Language
money, cost, estimate, 24-hour clock, timetable, time line, calculate

Resources
PCM 23 (one per pair)
PCM 24 (one per pair)

Setting the scene

Give out PCM 23 and go through the activity together. Explain that Dan and Lucy are on a coach trip to the beach with their family. They are given £10 each to spend, and have a variety of activities to choose from. Point out the coach ticket with arrival and departure times and also the time for lunch. Explain that they will be working in pairs to plan the day for the two children.

Getting started

Ask the children what other information is needed. They should come up with the fact that we don't know much about the children which makes it difficult to work out what they would enjoy. Give out PCM 24 and go through the short list about both children. This should help inform the judgements, but explain that there is no set solution. Each pair works out a plan for the day, making sure that no more than £10 is spent.

Simplify

Rather than planning a day for Dan and Lucy, the pairs could work out a day at the beach for themselves. They then need simply to think of the things that they would enjoy, whilst still working out the time and the costs involved with the activities.

Challenge

More activities could be included, so that there is a wider selection of times and prices. This could include mini-golf, bouncy castle, funfair rides etc. The pairs then need to make the day as active and full as possible with a £20 limit. You could get them to add a fortune line or mood graph to the task to evaluate if the money is well spent!

Checkpoints

Watch out for ...

Some of the times are in 24-hour and some in 12-hour time, so the children may need a little support if they struggle with this. The recording of times and amounts spent may be a little tricky to organize. PCM 24 gives one way of recording the time line, but the children may wish to sort it out in a different way.

Ask ...
- Have you used all the information?
- Why do you think this is the best solution?
- Could you alter it to improve it?

Listen for ...

The children may need to work out a rough timetable first and then refine it. They need to be able to empathize with Dan and Lucy and plan a suitable and enjoyable day for each, so expect children to argue and justify their choices and decisions.

Moving on ...

Ask pairs to compare their time lines and costs. Are any similar, or do the results vary? Talk about the activities chosen for each child and listen to pairs justifying their decisions. Check the accuracy and quality of the presentation of the results.

Where next?
- Use holiday brochures to plan a day trip or holiday. Give a budget and time constraints and compare the resulting choices.
- Ask the children to record a day at the weekend as a time line. Use the information to carry out a survey and present findings using graphs and charts. *What percentage of time is spent eating? What fraction of your day do you watch TV?*
- You could combine this chart with a mood graph and get children to discuss the cost effectiveness of their spending!

How did the children approach the problem? Were they careful and well organized, using the information to inform their decisions? Did they work well together, helping each other to sort out the information? Were they regularly evaluating their results and altering and refining the day so that it improved, or were they satisfied with their first attempts? Was there evidence of them using and applying skills from earlier activities?

DEBRIEF

2 Basic information about mathematical objectives and language are included, along with any resources needed, plus the thinking skills focus.

5 The 'Getting started' section shows how the activity can be developed through collaborative group work.

7 Reviewing progress and stimulating further thinking are covered in the 'Moving on' section, as are suggestions to develop the teaching strategy or approach in other mathematics lessons, or in other subjects in 'Where next?'.

3 Each activity has accompanying photocopiable resources. Some are resource sheets for the activities, others aim to support the recording of the activities, particularly by pairs or small groups of pupils (for more information on recording see page 16).

Classroom management

Structure and timing of lessons

Each book in the *Thinking by Numbers* series comprises six units. These are based around the English National Curriculum thinking skills headings of **information processing, reasoning, enquiry, creative thinking** and **evaluation**, with a final unit focused on using and applying the skills acquired through the earlier activities. Each unit contains two activities, with three in the final 'using and applying' unit, giving a total of 13 thinking activities or lessons for each year group. They have been planned as mathematics lessons and cover aspects of the curriculum appropriate for each age group (see the NNS and *Mathematics 5–14* matching charts on pages 90 to 95). You could also use the activities as thinking lessons and follow the suggestions at the end of each unit to develop the ideas and thinking strategies across the curriculum. When planning how to use the activities there are a number of different approaches you could take, and these are outlined here.

Regular thinking skills development

You could work through the activities using a *Thinking by Numbers* activity every two or three weeks. The benefit of this approach is that it provides regular opportunities to highlight the thinking skills you want to develop across the year. In the intervening time you would need to make sure that you refer back to the lessons and activities, as it would be all too easy for your pupils, particularly younger children, to forget what you are looking for in their work in the thinking activities.

Intensive thinking skills development

You could choose to work through the units more intensively, perhaps one activity each week over a term, so that you could then take the skills and ideas further over the course of the year. This may also be more suitable for year groups in England where your teaching is affected by statutory tests, such as Year 6 in particular. A further advantage of this approach is that you can build up some momentum with regular 'thinking maths' lessons. Assuming they go well initially, the children will start to look forward to the lessons and you can then capitalize on this enthusiasm. You will also

develop a language around the lessons and activities with your class, and the regular practice will enhance this development.

Integrated thinking skills development

Another possible approach for teachers in England and Scotland is to use the matching charts to the *NNS Framework* or *Mathematics 5–14*. These are provided in the appendices and will enable you to substitute the *Thinking by Numbers* activities where they fit most appropriately in your usual teaching plan. Whilst this is less disruptive to the mathematics curriculum, you will need to work hard to develop the thinking themes in the book. The thinking skills issue here is how you get the children to use what they learn elsewhere. This is always a challenge with any learning at school: how do you get learners to transfer what they know or can do to a new situation? The concept of 'bridging' is a useful one. As a teacher you connect or 'bridge' the knowledge or skills between different contexts. Where you have regular lessons you can mention things that you then refer to in other lessons. The further apart the sessions, the harder you will have to work to make those connections meaningful. *You remember when we used a Venn diagram to look at similarities and differences? Could we do something similar here?*

Managing the lesson

To use the *Thinking by Numbers* activities effectively you will need to think through the method of working. Your pupils will need to have a clear idea of what they are doing, and why, so that in the review sections of the lesson they can evaluate how successful they have been. It is important to get the lessons off to a good start, so the children will need a 'hook' or some initial stimulus to launch into the activity well. This can be either through the way you introduce the activity, the resources that are used, or perhaps the way you make it meaningful to the pupils, tapping into their particular interests or enthusiasms. It is hard to predict exactly how long the different activities will take to complete. Sometimes children become particularly enthusiastic about a particular task and you will struggle to get through everything that is suggested. On other occasions you will have time to review the activities and ask the children to reflect on their learning.

Introducing the lesson

Each activity begins with some kind of whole class introduction or demonstration. In this part of the lesson it is important to explain the activity and its purpose clearly. You should make objectives explicit; explain what you want from the pupils in terms of how they should work and the kind of language they should use. You will need to get feedback from the pupils to evaluate whether they understand what they are doing and know what they will have to do in the next phase of the activity. You may also need to adapt the activities according to the needs of your pupils. Although the activities have been designed for particular ages of pupils, you will need to judge whether some alteration is needed to provide the appropriate level of challenge for your class.

During the lesson

In most of the activities the pupils apply or extend the ideas presented in the introduction by working collaboratively in pairs or small groups. When moving from whole-class to paired or group work, it is useful to discuss or mention how the pairs or groups are going to work together and what you are looking for. At the transition it is worth praising specific behaviours: *I liked the way you sorted out the number cards for your group, David.* Though it is also important to tailor this praise, particularly for older pupils who should be aware of supportive behaviours and active listening strategies: *Your group got started really quickly, Emma, what was it that you each did?* Reinforce the method of sharing ideas, explaining that they can do better together than they can separately, and that copying and ownership of ideas are not factors. The tasks themselves are designed to be challenging and to benefit from some discussion in small groups so that pupils don't just make up their minds quickly. The activities also contain suggestions for differentiation, with advice on simplifications and challenges that should help you to ensure that the level of challenge is maintained as the pupils work through the tasks. Further advice on

the opportunities to develop speaking and listening skills are outlined on pages 18 and 19.

Reviewing the lesson

The hardest part of these activities is in helping pupils to see that particular tactics, strategies or approaches are helpful, without teaching specific solutions or answers. This will require some skilful questioning and discussion. It is important to review both the process that the pupils have used, particularly the collaborative skills of speaking and listening, as well as reviewing the curriculum content and knowledge and understanding of the activities.

It is also a good idea to review some of this as the lesson unfolds, rather than waiting until the end. Whilst the plenary seems to be the logical place to review the lesson, the pupils also know that the lesson is drawing to an end and it can be hard to maintain their interest. Mini-plenaries are, therefore, an essential teaching strategy which can help make the activities successful. These can be very brief, just checking where groups are up to, or sharing a successful technique or tactic being used by some children. *I noticed you've sorted the cards into different groups, can you tell the class how they are organized?* It boosts their confidence if you draw this to the attention of the whole class and gives other pupils who may not be on track a clear hint about what they could do.

Another possibility is to recap at the beginning of the next lesson. This is essential if the *Thinking by Numbers* sessions are a week or more apart. You need to remind the children that these are different lessons which require thinking, explaining, reasoning and evaluating. There should be more time for discussion about what went well previously and what skills or strategies they might find useful. The main aim is to help the pupils understand that they might not be able to see a solution immediately, but by thinking and working together they will be able to complete the activity successfully. In mathematics this is particularly important as it is a subject which pupils tend to think that they are either good at or not good at, rather than a subject that they can all learn to be better at!

Formative assessment and assessment for learning

Formative assessment is about intervening during teaching to improve learning. As a teacher you gather feedback about what is going on (either within a lesson or between lessons) and use that information to alter what you do subsequently. Assessment for learning is a more interactive approach that takes assessment a stage further by involving the learners in understanding what the specific learning objectives are for each activity/task/lesson so that they can judge how successful they have been in achieving them. This helps teachers and pupils to understand the criteria for being successful at learning, both for short term objectives as well as longer term goals about 'learning to learn' more effectively.

When assessing for learning it is important to give pupils feedback about what they can do to improve (rather than giving marks or feedback that simply indicates whether they are correct or not). One common technique is to get pupils to give you feedback about how well they think they are doing on an activity or a piece of work. This can be a simple thumbs up/down signal from the class, or getting pupils to use traffic light colours to self-assess a piece of work they have done – green for go ('I understand it and can go on'), orange for getting there ('I could do with a little bit of help'), red for stop ('I'm stuck').

Thinking skills approaches also involve formative assessment. Most of the activities are about giving you, the teacher, information about children's thinking. This lets you assess their understanding and make decisions about how to support the development of that thinking. In addition, pupils are expected to talk about their thinking as they undertake the tasks. Developing this metacognitive talk (talk about their own thinking) is a powerful technique which helps learners understand their learning better.

Furthermore, focusing on what makes for successful learning encourages judgement about that learning and moves the discussion away from the products

or outputs (such as a complete page of calculations) to what has been learned (such as, 'I am finding subtraction more difficult than addition'). The concept of transfer is crucial here since it moves learning away from the particular to the more general. *What have you learned today that you can use in the future? What have you learned previously that will help you now?*

Both assessment for learning and thinking skills approaches use collaborative techniques for learning: paired and group work so that learners benefit from discussion with their peers. Both approaches highlight the role of the teacher in effective questioning and discussions with the pupils to move their thinking on. Assessment for learning and thinking skills approaches are clearly complementary. If you are developing formative assessment you will be developing children's thinking skills. If you are developing children's thinking skills and being explicit about the thinking they are doing with them, then this is formative assessment!

Suggestions for further reading

Primary National Strategy, *Excellence and Enjoyment: learning and teaching in the primary years. Planning and assessment for learning: assessment for learning* (Document code: DfES 0521-2004 G) (2004)

Assessment Reform Group, *Assessment for Learning: 10 principles* (London, QCA, 2002) (available online at: http://www.qca.org.uk/ages3-14/downloads/afl_principles.pdf)

P. Black, C. Harrison, C. Lee, B. Marshall and D. William, *Assessment for Learning. Putting it into practice.* (Maidenhead, Open University Press, 2003)

S. Clarke, *Unlocking Formative Assessment: Practical strategies for enhancing pupils' learning in the primary classroom* (London, Hodder and Stoughton, 2001)

How do you know it is working?

One of the greatest challenges in developing learners' thinking is assessing how well the activities are going. You should feel that the tasks and activities are giving the children opportunities to think and you should get direct and indirect evidence of this. There are a number of ways that you can start to gauge the impact of the activities.

Enjoyment

First and foremost the activities should be enjoyable, both for you and your class. It is important that the activities are regarded as fun because this helps the children to develop their confidence to discuss what they think. It encourages the children to offer opinions and ideas without the worry of being 'wrong'. This aspect of the activities is vital to ensure their success. Thinking is hard work, so it needs to be as enjoyable as possible!

Participation

Enjoyment should lead to increased engagement and involvement in the lessons. One of the ways that you can assess this is by keeping track of who participates. Are the contributions coming from those who are usually involved and usually speak in whole class discussions? Can you use the paired or group work to build pupils' confidence in contributing to a whole class discussion? *I thought that your suggestion was a really good one – can you explain it to the class?* Are you getting spontaneous contributions from those you normally have to ask directly?

Language

The next thing to watch for is language that indicates thinking and reasoning. Are the pupils giving reasons? Do they use words like *then, so, because*? Are they being tentative (*I think … It could be … It might be …*) or speculative (*What if …? How about if we …?*)? You can start the lesson by saying you want to hear particular phrases, and giving suggestions for how they may be used. Then you need to look out for these first when the children are working in pairs or small groups. Then encourage the children to give longer responses in class discussions, ask them for reasons or examples, or to comment on each other's ideas. One of the most effective ways of encouraging this is simply to wait longer when you ask a question, and wait a little bit longer at the end of the response whilst indicating that you want them to continue. In mathematics you should also see the children using specific vocabulary more precisely; for example, are they getting more accurate in the use of words like *number, numeral* and *digit*? Or terms like *side, corner, edge* and *vertex*? You should also pay attention to the questions that the children ask. If the lessons are successful, the children will be asking questions about the content of the learning (rather than just about what they have to do).

Reflection

If the activities are working the children should know that they have been successful and that they have been thinking hard. They should show growing awareness of this and be able to talk about their thinking. At first this will come out during the activities or just as you finish. It is a good tactic to get them to review and reflect at the beginning of the next *Thinking by Numbers* task; this will help remind them of what is expected in the next task as well as giving you a chance to assess how much they recall from last time!

Transfer

The long term goal of *Thinking by Numbers* is to develop transferable skills. Evidence of this is shown when children start to refer back to thinking skills activities in terms of what they have learned. You should, therefore, begin to notice that they are using and talking about the skills that they are developing in other maths lessons or in other subjects. If this is spontaneous or unprompted you know that they are using the thinking skills for themselves.

Recording

Opportunities for recording are identified in most of the activities. However, there are a number of issues you will need to consider. The activities are about developing thinking and the lesson must focus on this as the most important outcome. Recording can distract from this if the children become concerned with making sure they 'get it right' when they have to write something down. There are two main aspects of recording. The first is the recording of the particular task. Some of the photocopiable resources are explicitly designed for this. For other activities the children will need to think about the best way to record their thinking and their progress through the activity. The activities are often collaborative so you may need to make copies of the completed sheet for all the children in the group.

The second aspect of recording is to support review of the activities. The 'What did you learn today?' photocopiable sheet (see page 17) is designed to help with this. It may not be appropriate to use it for every activity, but it will help you review aspects of the lesson that enable the children to develop an understanding of their thinking and their learning (see *Formative assessment and assessment for learning* on page 14 for more information about developing thinking about learning). This aspect is cumulative and progressive as you will need to encourage the children to think about:

- their learning
- what they did
- what kind of thinking was involved
- how they worked together
- what lessons or skills they have learned that they can use in the future.

When planning how to incorporate recording into a thinking lesson, it is helpful to consider the following principles.

1 Recording should be purposeful
The record should either help with the process of the task or capture aspects of the thinking that it will be helpful to review.

2 Recording should be integral
If keeping track of what they are doing is not part of the task, it becomes an extra burden and less likely to be completed effectively.

3 Recording should be used
If you ask the children to make some notes on their thinking, or to use the 'What did you learn today?' PCM, you need to make use of it in a discussion either in that lesson or as part of setting the scene for the next activity.

4 Recording should be short
The lessons are about thinking and this needs to be the most important part of the lesson. You will not be able to capture everything that happens; you may need to have some kind of record to keep track of what has happened, but keep it as simple as possible.

What did you learn today?

Name _____ Date _____

What did you learn today? _____

_____

_____

What kind of thinking did you do today?

	Yes	No
I remembered things that were useful	☐	☐
I organized my ideas	☐	☐
I thought of reasons why	☐	☐
I found out something I did not know	☐	☐
I used a rule or a pattern to work something out	☐	☐
I had a new idea which was helpful	☐	☐
I was methodical	☐	☐

How challenging was it?

Circle one of the choices on the line.

Very easy   Easy   OK   Hard   Very hard

Working with others

	Yes	No
I asked my teacher a good question	☐	☐
I asked a question which helped my partner	☐	☐
I asked a question which helped my group	☐	☐
I shared my ideas	☐	☐
I changed my mind after listening to someone	☐	☐
I was good at listening to my partner	☐	☐

Speaking and listening

Talking, thinking and learning are all closely related. We can remember things that we have heard, but it is only when we can put these ideas into our own words that we know we have learned them effectively. Speaking and listening are, therefore, at the heart of any thinking skills work. Listening to your pupils talk is also the best feedback you can get to assess what they are actually learning. It is therefore essential that the lessons and activities have speaking and listening at their core.

Children should be able to explain not just what they are doing, but why, and that their thinking is about the learning they are involved in. This involves speaking, listening and participating effectively in small and large group discussions. This helps them to learn by using new vocabulary (or words they already know more accurately) to express new ideas and new thinking. This process is difficult and requires time and support. Part of the purpose of the group work is to allow this to happen. Children will hear their peers making suggestions and having ideas about the tasks. As they join in and make their own suggestions they will work together to find a solution. This will help Children succeed more independently in future tasks. The discussions with the whole class will help them to be more confident in what they are saying and thinking, and will give you opportunities to provide feedback on what you are looking for in thinking lessons. The table on page 19 sets out a progression in speaking, listening and group discussion and interaction across the primary age range.

Classroom language

Classroom language is like a dialect of English. It has particular features and implicit rules that are different from language outside of school. The way you take turns, as a pupil, is very different from the way you normally take turns in conversation, either with your friends or at home. The teacher's use of questions, in particular, is strikingly different. Questions are often heavily loaded. For example, if you ask 'Why did you write that?', a child may assume that you are challenging them because it is incorrect and that they should have put something else. In a thinking skills lesson you may be wanting them to explain the reasons for their choices, or the decisions they made about what to write down, so as to provide a model for the rest of the class. If a teacher asks 'What do you *think* you should do?', the pupils may assume that you are reprimanding them for not listening, rather than asking them to speculate. It is therefore very important to think carefully about the questions that you ask to try to ensure that your pupils understand you really *do* want to know what they are thinking! Some examples of good questions are provided on page 21.

Talking maths

Mathematical language is also different from everyday English. It is important that children do not just learn and remember the vocabulary, but learn how to use the language to communicate. This will help them to develop their mathematical thinking. Many words have specialist meanings in maths lessons, such as 'odd' and 'even'. Other words may not be encountered outside of these lessons, for example, 'trapezium' and 'numerator'. The *Thinking by Numbers* activities are a chance for children to speak the language of mathematics, rather than just practise its vocabulary.

Suggestions for further reading
Primary National Strategy, *Speaking, Listening, Learning: Working with children in Key Stages 1 and 2. Professional development materials* (Document code: DfES 0163-2004) (2004)

N. Mercer, *Words and Minds: How We Use Language To Think Together* (London, Routledge, 2000)

S. Higgins, *Parlez-vous mathematics? Enhancing Primary Mathematics Teaching and Learning*, I. Thompson (ed.) (Buckingham, Open University Press, 2003)

A skills progression in ...

	... Speaking	... Listening	... Group discussion and interaction
Y1/2	▶ Speak clearly and expressively in supportive contexts on a familiar topic. ▶ Order talk reasonably and pace well when recounting events or actions. ▶ Talk engagingly to listeners with emphasis and varied intonation. ▶ Able to use gestures and visual aids to highlight meanings.	▶ Listen actively following practical consequences, e.g.: – looking at a speaker – asking for repetition if needed. ▶ Able to clarify and retain information: – by acting on instructions – by rephrasing in collaboration with others – by asking for more specific information.	▶ Talk purposefully in pairs and small groups. ▶ Contribute ideas in plenary and whole-class discussions. ▶ Make and share predictions, take turns, contribute to review of group discussion. ▶ Review and comment on effectiveness of group discussions.
Y3/4	▶ Sustain speaking to a range of listeners, explaining reasons, or why something interests them. ▶ Organize and structure subject matter of their own choice, and pace their talk (including pauses for interaction with listeners) for emphasis and meaning. ▶ Adapt talk to the needs of the listeners (such as to visitors or more formal contexts), showing awareness of standard English.	▶ Sustain listening independently and make notes about what different speakers say, identifying the gist, key ideas and links between them. ▶ Able to comment and respond, evaluating a speaker's contribution, or evaluate quality of information provided. ▶ Able to concentrate in different contexts, including talk without/by actions and visual aids.	▶ Sustain different roles in group work (with support from a teacher), including leading and summarizing main reasons for a decision. ▶ Talk about language needed to carry out such roles and how they contribute to the overall effectiveness of the work. ▶ Reflect constructively on strengths and weaknesses of group talk.
Y5/6	▶ Develop ideas in extended turns for a range of purposes. ▶ Assimilate information from different sources and contrasting points of view, present ideas in ways appropriate to spoken language. ▶ Use features of standard English appropriately in more formal contexts. ▶ Make connections and organize thinking.	▶ Listen actively and selectively for content and tone. ▶ Able to distinguish different registers, moving between formal and informal language according to the audience, and emphasize or undercut surface meanings. ▶ Able to discern different threads in an argument or the nuances in talk.	▶ Organize and manage collaborative tasks over time and in different contexts with minimal supervision. ▶ Negotiate disagreements and possible solutions, by clarifying the extent of differences, or by putting ideas to the vote. ▶ Vary the register and precision of their language and comment on the choices made in more formal contexts.

Adapted from Primary National Strategy, *Speaking, Listening, Learning: Working with children in Key Stages 1 and 2 Handbook* (Norwich, DfES/HMSO, 2003)

Collaborative group work

Collaborative group work is an essential part of thinking skills teaching. The opportunity to work with a partner or in a small group is essential. This is where children can explore their own thinking, hear other people's ideas, be tentative, make mistakes, but be supported and encouraged by their peers. This is how an individual develops confidence in new ways of thinking. However, it does not happen automatically. You will need to make time for it, support, nurture and encourage it.

Plan for it

Thinking about who is going to work with whom, and how, is essential. It won't just happen until the class are used to this way of working, and even then there will be new skills they can develop. Most thinking skills lessons are based on mixed groups that are not based on current levels of attainment. However, you will need to monitor who works well with whom and support the children in working with a wider range of their peers.

Make it explicit

The children need to know that they are expected to work together, and that you are expecting them to help each other. This needs continual reinforcement with the whole class in the introduction, mini-plenaries and review sections of lessons (praising and reminding groups and individuals helps, too).

Teach pupils how to work in groups

Not all children find it easy to cooperate. They may well need the first few activities to focus on learning to work together. It is worth making this a part of your learning objectives for speaking and listening (see pages 18 to 19). In one of the early sessions (if you have not done so already), it is worth agreeing class rules for working in groups or a 'working together protocol'. Such an agreement should be phrased positively about what children should do and might include things like:

- Make sure everybody has a turn in speaking
- One person speaks at a time
- Look at the person who is talking (make eye contact)
- Listen actively (positive body language such as nodding or an open posture)
- Speak clearly
- Explain what you mean
- Respond to what other people say
- Make a longer contribution than just one or two words
- Give reasons for what you think
- Make it clear when you disagree that it is with what has been said (with your reasons) and not a person.

However, it is important that the precise wording comes from the children and that the agreement is posted publicly where it will always be visible in the classroom. The children will use it!

Start small

Pairs are the easiest groups to start with. In Key Stage 1 this should be the main aim. Even very young children should be able to cooperate in pairs, particularly if the cooperation is structured in some way (such as taking turns in a game). Moving from pairs to fours is a good tactic too. A paired task can be reviewed by two pairs to reach agreement, then this larger grouping can form the basis for a further activity.

Make sure the tasks require cooperation

Consider strategies such as having one recording sheet, or set of resources that need to be shared, or assign specific tasks to each member of the group. As groups get bigger you may need to assign different roles and let the children practise the different skills required (for example, leader, note taker, summarizer, clarifier). In the beginning it is best to use existing friendships as the basis for organizing the groups, but don't let them get too cosy. Learning to work with people who are not close friends is an important skill for life!

> **Suggestions for further reading**
> L. Dawes, N. Mercer and R. Wegerif, *Thinking Together: Activities for teachers and children at Key Stage 2* (Birmingham, Questions Publishing Co., 2000)

Talking points

Getting started

How are you going to tackle this?
What information have you got to help you?
What do you need to find out or do?
How are you going to do it? Why that way?
Can you think of any questions you will need to ask?
What do you think the answer or result will look like?
Can you make a prediction?

Supporting progress

Can you explain what you have done so far?
What else do you need to do?
Can you think of another way that might have worked?
What do you mean by ...?
What did you notice when ...?
Are you beginning to see a pattern or a rule?

If someone is stuck ...

Can you say what you have to do in your own words?
Can you talk me through where you are up to?
Is there something that you know already that might help you?
How could you sort things out to help you?
Would a picture help, or a table/sketch/diagram/graph?
Have you talked with your partner/another pair/group about what they are doing?

Reviewing learning

What have you learned today?
What would you do differently if you were doing this again?
When could you use this approach/idea again?
What are the key points or ideas that you need to remember?
Did it work out the way you expected?
How did you check it?

Remember – one way to ask a question is just to wait!

Suggestions for further reading
Association of Teachers of Mathematics (2004)
Primary Questions and Prompts Derby: ATM

Thinking skills across the curriculum

There are a number of general teaching strategies that you can explore to support the activities in *Thinking by Numbers*. They are helpful because you can use the same technique in different contexts and develop thinking across the curriculum. Each time you use these strategies you can focus on the children's thinking that you want to develop. The children become familiar with the techniques and can get straight down to the learning involved. The strategies are also useful in assessing the children's understanding. If you first **demonstrate** a technique or approach, you can then set an activity which the children **undertake** to develop their thinking. This is as far as most approaches to thinking skills go. However if you then set a challenge where the children have to **generate** their own activity based on what they have done, you will see them reveal their understanding of the thinking required. This cycle of **demonstrate**, **undertake** and **generate** ensures that the thinking becomes embedded.

Odd one out

In this strategy the children are presented with three items and asked to choose one as the 'odd one out' and to give a reason. Items are chosen to ensure that a range of answers are possible. Pupils can also be asked to identify the similar corresponding characteristic of the other two, or features common to all, to develop their vocabulary and understanding. In mathematics this leads naturally on to a discussion of the properties of numbers and to identifying numbers which have a range of properties. It can easily be extended to work on shapes or into other subjects. Selecting three items with different possible reasons is essential. When the children design their own game it is essential that you emphasize that there should be more than one solution or 'answer'. It leads on to identifying common properties that the odd one out lacks.

Living graphs

The strategy involves a graph or a chart as the basis for an activity where the children have to relate short statements to the more abstract structure of a graph. The use of statements that children can understand easily, but which they then have to discuss and interpret, helps them to make sense of both the representation of the graph and the information it is based on. This works well in mathematics and science, but also in other subjects where quantitative information is used, such as history and geography.

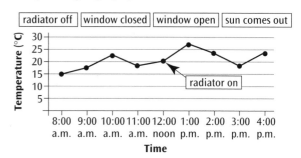

Always, sometimes, never

Another useful strategy is to have a set of statements, such as 'triangles have three sides' or 'multiples of 3 are odd' and ask the children if they are 'always' true, 'sometimes' true or 'never' true. This works well in mathematics and science: in other subjects you may need to set these categories along a continuum to provoke discussion.

As before, asking the children to make up statements that are always, sometimes or never true is a good way to extend the task (and their thinking).

Think/Pair/Share

This is a good general technique to get everyone thinking. Instead of getting a response from an individual pupil ask the whole class to work out the answer, then see if the person next to them agrees, then ask each pair to discuss what they have agreed with another pair. A further variation gets the children to record their thinking before discussing it with a partner 'Think/Ink/Pair/Share'.

Fermi questions

The approach of Enrico Fermi, who was an Italian scientist who used to pose questions to get his team thinking and working together, works well in the classroom. At school a question such as: *How many balloons would it take to fill the school hall?* requires the children to ask a number of related questions along the lies of, *How big is a balloon? How big is the hall?* This particularly develops estimation and approximation skills. Discussion and reasoning is an important part of the process of answering them. Other questions might be: *How many chocolate beans will it take to fill a litre lemonade bottle? What is the total mass of all the children in the school? Or If everyone in school (or the class) lay down in a line from the school gate (or classroom door), head to toe, where would the line end?* Once the children get used to answering questions like this you can ask them to think up their own.

Banned!

Another strategy uses an approach that involves describing an idea or object without using certain banned words (the Association of Teachers of Mathematics [ATM] have a mathematical version called 'Fourbidden'). This can be used to develop creative use of language to describe familiar ideas and concepts. This strategy works well across the curriculum and can be used to get children thinking creatively about their use of language.

describe:	without using:
a square	four sides shape equal

PMI

PMI stands for 'Plus/Minus/Interesting' and is a technique developed by Edward de Bono (as part of his Cognitive Research Trust [CoRT] programme) to get beyond the basic 'pros and cons' approach and the snap decisions that can result from this. When there is a difficult decision or where evaluation is needed, draw up a table headed up 'Plus', 'Minus', and 'Interesting'. In the column underneath the 'Plus' heading, ask the children to write down all the positive points of taking the action. Underneath the 'Minus' heading they write down all the negative points. In the 'Interesting' column they write any further thoughts that strike them. These can be scored across the class to find out how many plus and minus points there are as a method of voting.

Mind-mapping and Concept-mapping

In 'Mind mapping' the children are asked to brain storm an idea or a concept to create a web of related ideas with branches for each related sub idea. It can be used in a wide variety of ways. Mind mapping is usually done individually as a means to represent thinking on a topic, either to record ideas or so that the connections between ideas can be developed. In 'Concept-mapping' the links between the different ideas on the 'map' are labelled so that the relationship between the ideas is expressed more precisely. This supports clarification and developing understanding of the relationships between ideas. Concept Mapping has been used across the curriculum, but particularly in science, as a way of assessing change in understanding by pupils.

Activities in this book

Unit 1 Sort it out! *Information processing skills*	**The matrix (pages 26–29)** Children place the numbers 1 to 20 into matrices according to their attributes. They need to identify and discuss properties of the numbers according to their positions, as there may be more than one possible solution. **Cake stall (pages 30–33)** This is a problem-solving activity where the children complete a timetable for the cake stall at a village fête from the information that they are given. There is no set solution and flexible thinking is needed.
Unit 2 That's because … *Reasoning skills*	**Mood graphs (pages 36–39)** The children are asked to draw a graph that represents a child's feelings over the course of the day. They explain and give reasons for their opinions in order to justify their thinking. **Crossing the river (pages 40–43)** A version of the classic puzzle where children have to use their reasoning skills to work out how many crossings are needed to carry one boy and two girls across a river. The children describe the number patterns they find and identify generalizations.
Unit 3 Detective work *Enquiry skills*	**The birthday present (pages 46–49)** The children are presented with a letter from outlining a choice of five ways that Bernard could be given some money. They make a decision about which scheme to choose and then reply on his behalf. **Giant feet (pages 50–53)** An enquiry about 'how much space do you have in your shoe?' leads on to an investigation of the size of a giant's foot.
Unit 4 What if …? *Creative thinking skills*	**Washing machines (pages 56–59)** The children investigate the relationship between the choices on different washing machine models and the number of programmes resulting from these combinations. The children think of ways to organize and present their findings so that they can recognize any patterns in their results. **Spiral paths (pages 60–63)** An open-ended shape investigation that starts from a 90° spiral repeat of three lines. Children work in pairs or small groups to create and explore a range of different spirals.
Unit 5 In my opinion … *Evaluation skills*	**Holiday hot spots (pages 66–69)** Using information about two seaside resorts the children choose a resort that would be best for certain groups of people and design an advertising leaflet for their chosen group. **Birdwatching (70–73)** In this 'mystery' the children are given a real news report about a rare bird and then using a set of clues they work as a group to decide whether a birdwatcher will have enough time to see the bird before it is unfortunately caught by a sparrowhawk.
Unit 6 Think on! *Using and applying thinking skills*	**Discs (pages 76–79)** An investigation where children work out numbers from given totals. The children think of different strategies to narrow the possibilities. **Day trip to the beach (p 80–83)** Children organize and evaluate information to plan a good day out at the beach for a brother and sister. **Radio waves (pages 84–87)** A classic maths investigation based on connecting rows of houses to two radio masts to identify intersections in order to recognize patterns in the solutions that can be generalized.

Sort it out!

Information processing skills

> **Information processing** – these skills enable pupils to locate and collect relevant information, to sort, classify, sequence, compare, contrast and analyze part/whole relationships. (QCA 2000)

Overview

This unit is about working with mathematical ideas and concepts by gathering information. It is about building understanding by actively working with these concepts and ideas. It is about remembering links and making connections to understand what information is relevant. It is also about working with ideas to develop understanding of their meaning by working with patterns and rules, working with definitions and organizing and representing ideas. It is an essential aspect of mathematical thinking. The activities in this unit are designed to help pupils engage practically with ideas and information so as to build their knowledge and understanding of mathematical concepts.

Strategies

Information processing skills can be broken down further into the following kinds of behaviours or activities that pupils can do:

◐ **Find relevant information**
   Remember, recall, search, recognize, identify
◐ **Collect relevant information**
   Retrieve, identify, select, gather, choose
◐ **Sort**
   Group, include, exclude, list, make a collection or set
◐ **Classify**
   Sort, order, arrange *by kind or type*
◐ **Sequence**
   Order, arrange *by quantity/size/weight*, put in an array
◐ **Compare**
   Find similarities/differences, examine, relate, liken
◐ **Contrast**
   Find differences/and similarities, examine, distinguish
◐ **Analyze part/whole relationships**
   Relate, consider, sort out, make links *between parts and wholes* (e.g. component/integral object (such as the face of a cube); member/collection; portion/mass; stuff/object; place/area; feature/activity; especially in terms of fractions, ratios and the like).

Questions

Can you think of something that might help? What does this remind you of?
Give me an example of a ... Is ... an example? Can you give a counter-example?
What would come next? What would come before this?
Why is it the same/different? What makes it a ...? What is it like? What makes a ... different from a ...?

The matrix

'The matrix' involves the children working with matrices in two ways. In the first, the attributes of the matrix are given so that the children decide on the possible positions of the numbers. They need to talk about the properties of numbers and justify their positions, as there may be more than one possible solution. The second involves a matrix with the numbers in place but no attributes. This makes the children identify properties rather than just recognize them.

Key maths links

- Properties of numbers
- Reasoning about numbers

Thinking skills

- Information processing
- Working with patterns and rules
- Reasoning

Language

odd, even, multiple, factor, square number, grid, greater than (>), less than (<), matrix, matrices

Resources

PCM 1 (one per pair)
PCM 2 (one per pair)
scissors

1 Setting the scene

Display a 3 × 3 grid with attribute labels [see 1 below]. Ask the children to give examples of numbers from 1 to 20 for each of the attributes that can fit on the matrix or grid, following each of the rules. Talk about the possible solutions. *Which numbers can be used in more than one square? Are there any numbers that cannot fit?* Display another 3 × 3 grid with the numbers written in [2]. Ask the children to work in pairs to decide on the missing attribute labels for the matrix. After a few minutes talk about the results as a class. *Are there any rows or columns that could have more than one label? Which were the easiest labels to decide on?*

1

	Multiple of 5	<10	>12
Factor of 20			
Odd number			
Multiple of 2			

2

	>15	Multiple of 3	Square number
Odd number	17	15	9
Multiple of 2	18	6	4
Multiple of 4	20	12	16

2 Getting started

Give out PCM 1. Ask the children to work in pairs to arrange the numbers on the first matrix according to the rules shown by the labels. Remind them that there is not one definite position for each number. Talk about the strategies they may use. *Which columns or rows are good ones to start with? Why? Which numbers could go in many of the squares?* Repeat this for the second matrix. *Is this grid possible to complete? Which squares or numbers are impossible to place?*

PCM 2 has attribute labels for pairs to arrange to match a matrix of numbers. Explain that there are more labels than are needed and they need to look carefully at the properties of each row and column.

Simplify

Increase the range of numbers. The children can make more number cards so that they have the numbers 1 to 30 to work with. Give support by pointing out that some of the properties, such as 'square number' and 'multiple of 4' have fewer numbers to choose from, so it is useful to complete those rows first.

Challenge

Ask the children to limit the range of numbers from 1 to 16. *Is it possible to complete the matrix? Which squares are impossible?* The children could find out which numbers fit into the most squares and which numbers go into the fewest.

Checkpoints

It is important that the children arrange and rearrange the number cards and labels rather than writing them on the grid. However, they may wish to write lists of numbers possible in each square as a strategy for choosing numbers and then arrange the cards in suitable positions.

Watch out for ...

Check that there is no confusion with the < and > signs and that they don't confuse multiples and factors. Make sure the children realize that numbers and labels can possibly go in more than one position. Look for accurate use of language, particularly terms like 'multiple', 'factor' and 'square number'.

Ask ...

- ● *What if you moved that number?*
- ● *What have these numbers got in common?*
- ● *Why is that the best place for that number or label?*

Listen for ...

The children will be fully engaged in the activity if they find good reasons for positioning numbers and labels on the matrices and justify these reasons to their partner.

Moving on ...

Prompt the children to evaluate the different matrices and ask which were the most difficult to complete. Discuss the strategies used and ask if any children adopted a very systematic approach to completing the matrices. *Which strategies worked for you? Did you work well as a pair?*

Where next?

- ● Use the attribute labels and a blank 4 × 4 grid and ask children to design their own matrix puzzle. They can either make a blank grid with labels or a numbered grid with missing labels.
- ● Devise a 3 × 3 or 4 × 4 matrix with 2D or 3D shapes.
- ● Use the matrices on PCM 1 with a different range of numbers. Is it easier or more difficult with the numbers 51 to 70, for example?
- ● Use a matrix in another subject (such as properties of materials in science).

Which parts of this activity worked well? Did you feel the children were thinking about the best strategies to use or were they more interested in trying to complete the task? How well did the children work in pairs? What evidence of real thinking did you see or hear from the children?

DEBRIEF

Name _____   **Date** _____

Place the numbers on each matrix so they
follow the rules.

	Even number	Factor of 24	< 8	Odd number
< 12				
Multiple of 3				
Square number				
> 6				

	Odd number	> 10	Factor of 20	Multiple of 2
Square number				
Multiple of 5				
< 13				
Multiple of 3				

1	11
2	12
3	13
4	14
5	15
6	16
7	17
8	18
9	19
10	20

Thinking by Numbers 6 • **Unit 1: Sort it out!** • **Information processing skills**

Place the labels around the matrix so the numbers follow the correct rules.

2	11	12	6
5	19	3	15
4	16	9	1
8	20	18	10

✂

odd number	factor of 36	even number	factor of 40	multiple of 2
multiple of 3	triangular number	multiple of 4	prime number	multiple of 5
factor of 24	< 15	square number	> 10	

Cake stall

'Cake stall' is a problem-solving activity in which pieces of information are given about three children running a cake stall at a village fête. From this information a timetable chart needs to be completed so that all the details are correct. There is no set solution and flexible thinking is needed. You will be expecting the information to be considered, compared and sorted, through collaboration and discussion using a grid to help with the task. The activity also provides the opportunity for children to explain their thinking and justify reasons.

Key maths links

- Problems involving time and money
- Handling data – tables and charts

Thinking skills

- Information processing
- Ordering and sequencing
- Reasoning

Language

sort, order, represent, chart, table, o'clock, a.m., p.m., hour, timetable

Resources

PCM 3 (one per pair and/or one enlarged)
PCM 4 (one per pair)
scissors

 Setting the scene

Explain to the class that they will be helping sort out the timetable for a group of three children who have volunteered to run a cake stall at a village fête. They have been given a lot of information about how to organize their time, but they need help in making sure they use the time correctly. Show an enlarged copy of PCM 3 or ask the children to cut out the information cards. Ask pupils to read each card aloud to the class and discuss the information. Talk about the fact that individually these are easy to sort out, but putting all the information together so that all the criteria are satisfied is a lot trickier.

Getting started

Ask the children to work in pairs to use the information to sort out a timetable for the cake stall. They need the information cards from PCM 3 and the timetable chart from PCM 4. Check that they understand that there are many solutions and that they are looking for one that satisfies all the information given. Explain that the timetable chart is to display their final results, so they will need to work in draft at first, possibly on a further copy of this chart.

Simplify

To make the task easier, don't include the information card that states that all three children must spend the same amount of time on the stall. This makes the timetable a lot more flexible.

Challenge

The task is more challenging if the timetable chart isn't used. Pairs need to design their own recording chart or table to show the information.

 Checkpoints

Encourage the children to listen to each other and support each other in organizing and sorting the information. They may use strategies for sorting the criteria, such as finding the easiest to organize (e.g. Liam has to go home at 2:30 p.m.) and then using trial and improvement to fit the other criteria. Stop the class after approximately 10-15 minutes and ask them which of the pieces of information are causing the most difficulty. Listen to the strategies that the pairs are using.

Watch out for …

Check that the children don't get disheartened if the timetable takes many attempts to satisfy all the criteria. Trial and improvement by its nature involves correcting errors, so point out that this shows the thinking process.

Ask …

- ○ *What would be a good starting point?*
- ○ *How can you organize the information?*
- ○ *What if the timetable is incorrect? Can you slightly alter things or do you need to start again?*

Listen for …

The children that are prepared to make errors will succeed in this. Listen out for pairs that develop a 'rough' timetable and then compare the criteria while amending and improving the 'final' timetable. Are they only working from positive statements or are they using information about what can *not* be the case (such as blocking out Liam after 2:30 p.m.)?

4 Moving on …

Ask pairs to compare their timetables. Are any timetables similar, or was it possible to have a lot of variations in the results? Talk about the strategies used. Did any pairs sort out one child first, such as Liam, and build the other times around this? How did the grid help? Check the accuracy and quality of the presentation of the timetable chart.

Where next?

- ○ Ask pairs to devise a set of information cards for a different stall at the fête. They can make up different statements for others to use to complete a timetable. This will give you excellent feedback about how well they have understood the task.
- ○ Devise a set of information cards that deals with the money spent by each of the children on the stall. The problem could be linked to a timetable. For example:
  Jodie has double the money of Liam and £10 more than Kyle.
  In the first hour Liam spends half his money.
  At 2:30 p.m. Jodie buys a game for £6·75.
  Kyle starts with £8·20.

How did the children approach the problem? Were they systematic and well organized? Most importantly, did they work well together, helping each other to sort out the information? Perseverance is an important part of trial and improvement. How well did the children cope with this?

DEBRIEF

Jodie, Kyle and Liam are running a cake stall at their village fête.
Cut out and sort this information.

Liam has to go home at 2:30 p.m.

All three children must spend the same amount of time on the stall.

All breaks must be at least 30 minutes.

The village fête is from 10:00 a.m. to 4:00 p.m.

There must always be two children on the cake stall.

Each of them will have a break for lunch between 12:00 and 2:00 p.m.

No one should spend more than two hours at a time at the stall.

Cake stall timetable

Name _____ Date _____

Use the information from PCM 3 to work out a timetable.

	Jodie	Kyle	Liam
10:00 a.m. – 10:30 a.m.			
10:30 a.m. – 11:00 a.m.			
11:00 a.m. – 11:30 a.m.			
11:30 a.m. – 12:00 p.m.			
12:00 p.m. – 12:30 p.m.			
12:30 p.m. - 1:00 p.m.			
1:00 p.m. – 1:30 p.m.			
1:30 p.m. – 2:00 p.m.			
2:00 p.m. – 2:30 p.m.			
2:30 p.m. – 3:00 p.m.			
3:00 p.m. – 3:30 p.m.			
3:30 p.m. – 4:00 p.m.			

Use this key to fill in the timetable.

On the stall	colour red
Lunch break	colour blue
Looking around fête	colour yellow

Summary

Assessing progress

You know that children are developing their skills in information processing when they start to make connections with different mathematical ideas. They should start to show and use this understanding in other lessons. This might be by applying mathematical knowledge in a new situation or it might be in the way that they go about a subsequent task. As their skills in using information develop they should become more precise in the way that they use mathematical language and more systematic in their approach to working and to recording. The techniques that they have used should be developed in other subjects so that their understanding of information processing skills can be transferred to other areas of the curriculum.

Cross-curricular thinking

Literacy

A strategy like 'odd one out' can be used to compare characters from fictional genres, such as different heroines from traditional tales.

Art

The 'odd one out' strategy is also useful for comparing the work of famous artists or to look at similarities and differences in the visual and tactile qualities of materials.

Little Red Riding Hood, Snow White and Cinderella – who is the odd one out? Why? What makes the other two the same?

Science

Venn diagrams are powerful tools in the teaching of classification. This is particularly valuable in the strands of both variation and classification of living things, and materials and their properties.

History

Venn diagrams are useful to teach how to compare and contrast in history. Two intersecting sets can be used as a planning tool to identify similarities and differences between different historical periods. Common features go in the intersection and contrasting information on each side.

Geography

The 'odd one out' strategy and Venn diagrams are both helpful in geography. The former can be used to encourage children to use geographical vocabulary as they talk about what makes three different landscapes or features of the environment similar or different. The latter can be used for sorting pictures of buildings or vocabulary related to the character of places. This way, the children will develop an understanding of these concepts by having examples and counter-examples to talk about in a meaningful context.

That's because ...

Reasoning skills

> **Reasoning** – these skills enable pupils to give reasons for opinions and actions, to draw inferences and make deductions, to use precise language to explain what they think and to make judgements and decisions informed by reasons or evidence. (QCA 2000)

Overview

This unit is about reasoning and logical thinking. Reasoning is an essential aspect of mathematics and underpins the development of theorems and proofs through the use of precise definitions and axioms. For pupils of primary age it is important that they have the opportunity to apply their knowledge and understanding of mathematical ideas and concepts logically and systematically as this will enable them to make connections between different concepts and between different areas of mathematics. This will deepen their understanding and develop their confidence as well as helping them see how mathematics can be used as a practical tool in their daily lives.

Developing reasoning skills is also about developing habits of thinking or dispositions as much as it is about specific logical skills. Of course, just because you are good at reasoning does not mean that you are going to be reasonable. Part of thinking reasonably is also dependent upon your knowledge of yourself and the situation in which you find yourself. This metacognitive dimension is essential if you are going to help your pupils become effective thinkers and not just logical.

Strategies

Reasoning skills can be broken down further into the following kinds of behaviours or activities that pupils can do:
- **Give reasons for opinions and actions**
  explain, say because, say why
- **Draw inferences and make deductions**
  see links, make connections, infer, deduce, use words like 'so', 'then', 'must be', 'has to be'
- **Use precise language to explain what they think**
  exemplify, describe, define, characterize
- **Make judgements and decisions informed by reasons or evidence**
  form an opinion, determine, conclude, summarize, *especially where there is more than one course of action or possible solution*

Questions

Explain why ...? Can you give a reason ...? Because ... So ...
Why is ... an example? Is that always/sometimes/never true? What else must be true if ... ? Does it have to be like that? Can you define that? What do they all have in common?
What else is like that? What makes you say that? How can you be sure that ...?

Mood graphs

BRIEF

'Mood graphs' provides children with a Saturday timetable for Marcos and Rosa, and a line graph which shows the corresponding mood of Marcos. The children are then asked to draw a graph that they feel could represent Rosa's feelings. You will be looking for children making connections between the times given and the graph, and deductions from the evidence given. Encourage the children to explain and give reasons for their opinions.

Key maths links

- Measures – time
- Handling data – line graphs

Thinking skills

- Reasoning
- Drawing inferences and making deductions
- Make judgements informed by evidence

Language

line graph, axis, axes, timetable, interpret, represent

Resources

PCM 5 (one per child and/or one enlarged)
PCM 6 (one per pair)
graph paper

 Setting the scene

To introduce 'Mood graphs', draw a simple continuous time-line graph to show your moods for the day so far (make up events if necessary to make it interesting!). Discuss the highs and lows of your day and ask what sort of things may have happened. Display PCM 5 and the top graph of PCM 6 or give each child a sheet. Explain that Rosa and Marcos are sister and brother and the timetable shows details of the things they both did on a Saturday. Talk about the graph for Marcos and discuss the sorts of things he does and does not like doing: *What time is Marcos happiest? What does Marcos most like doing? What makes Marcos unhappy? Does Marcos enjoy bus journeys? What happened at 4:30 p.m.? What do you think could have happened at 10:30 a.m. to make him happy?*

 Getting started

Ask the children to work in pairs to draw a mood graph (also called a fortune line) for Rosa. Give a copy of PCM 6 to each pair and explain that they use the timetable of Rosa's Saturday and the list of her likes and dislikes to complete a graph. They can either draw new axes, or plot it over the graph for Marcos's feelings. Make sure they understand that the graph will be based on their opinions as well as the evidence provided, so there will be a variety of completed graphs.

Simplify

Read the times to the nearest hour. The children can draw small crosses at the high and low mood points based on the list given. They can then join the crosses to estimate Rosa's mood for the day.

Challenge

Ask the children to compare the two graphs and find out the joint high and low points for them during the day. Their mum is with them all day, so ask the children to talk about the graph for mum and to predict the reasons for the highs and lows in her day.

 Checkpoints

Check that children are connecting the information in the timetable to the line of the graph. They need to make decisions based on the information given which is sometimes vague and based on opinion.

Watch out for ...

Children may not understand the format of the continuous data on the graph.
If necessary, explain the difference between continuous and discrete data.
Some of the statements refer to a point in time (and are therefore on the graph),
others to a period of time: are the children distinguishing between these in
their discussions?

Ask ...

- *What made you think that this is correct?*
- *Why are you sure that ... is so happy then?*
- *Does everyone like swimming/hate washing up?*

Listen for ...

The children should be working collaboratively, justifying their opinions to their
partner. You may hear children using the words, 'because ...', 'why ...' and 'it must
be...'.

 Moving on ...

Compare the graphs and talk about the 'shapes' of each of the graphs. *Was there
enough information given to help you complete Rosa's graph?* Evaluate the success of
the cooperation between pairs. *Did you feel you worked well together? What would
your mood graph have looked like for the lesson?*

Where next?

- The children draw a mood graph for their Saturday. Once the graphs are
  drawn the rest of the class can try to work out what possible events happened
  during the day to cause the changes in mood. This can then be compared with
  the children's actual timetable.
- Use the data collected to develop a 'moods' database of favourite and least
  favourite activities.
- Develop the idea of mood graphs, or fortune lines, for a character in a story or
  a historical figure. This could be from a book children have read or a well-
  known character such as *Little Red Riding Hood*.

**Did the introduction motivate the children and explain the task clearly?
What evidence was there of reasoning and deductive thinking from the
children? Were the children confident in making judgements based on their
opinions and on the evidence given to them? What were the benefits of using
the visual support of the layout of the graph?**

DEBRIEF

This is how Marcos and Rosa spent their Saturday.

Time line	Marcos	Rosa
7:00 a.m.	wake up watch TV in bed	wake up
8:00 a.m.	wash	wash get dressed
9:00 a.m.	get dressed breakfast	breakfast
10:00 a.m.	play with puppy bus to town	listen to music bus to town
11:00 a.m.	shopping with mum	shopping with mum
Midday	lunch	lunch
1:00 p.m.	swimming	swimming
2:00 p.m.		
3:00 p.m.	bus home	bus home
4:00 p.m.	play with puppy tidy bedroom, watch TV	play out with friends
5:00 p.m.	tea	home tea
6:00 p.m.	wash up play out with friends	wash up read
7:00 p.m.	home watch TV	tidy bedroom listen to music/read
8:00 p.m.	wash bed/read a book	wash watch TV
9:00 p.m.		bed/read a book

Name _____ Date _____

Use the information to draw a mood graph for Rosa.

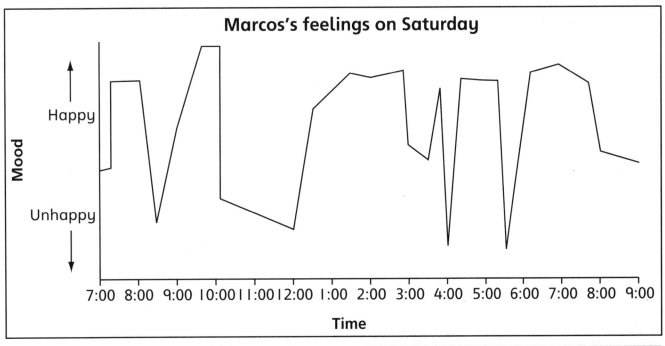

Marcos's feelings on Saturday

Rosa likes:
- reading
- music (a lot ...)
- clothes
- a tidy bedroom (!)
- friends
- her brother (sometimes)

Rosa does not like:
- buses
- waking up
- washing up
- going to bed
- watching TV
- her brother (sometimes)

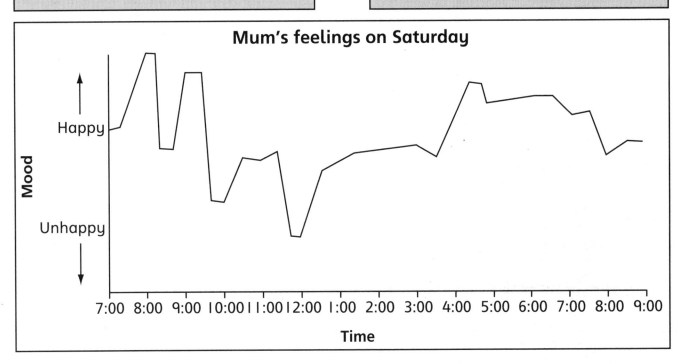

Mum's feelings on Saturday

Crossing the river

BRIEF

'Crossing the river' is a classic puzzle which can lead to some interesting number patterns and generalizations. In this version the children are asked to work out how many crossings are needed to carry one boy and two girls across a river. The boat can only hold *either* one girl *or* one boy *or* two girls at any one time and someone must return to pick up the person left behind. You will be looking for children that are able to describe any number patterns they find and explain any generalized rules.

Key maths links

- Reasoning about numbers
- Generalization and formulae

Thinking skills

- Reasoning and making deductions
- Logical thinking

Language

generalize, pattern, formula, investigate, predict

Resources

PCM 7 (one per pair and/or enlarged)
PCM 8 (one per pair)
counters (two colours)

1 Setting the scene

Display PCM 7 and ask the children if they can think of a good method for solving the problem; this may include using counters or actually moving children in the class. Ask a boy and two girls to come to the front of the class and model the problem, going across a 'river' until they have all crossed (5 trips altogether). Talk about ways of recording this. A possibility is:

→ 2 girls   ← 1 girl   → 1 boy   ← 1 girl   → 2 girls

2 Getting started

Give out PCM 8. Ask the children to work in pairs and explain that you want them to work out the number of trips needed to cross the river if there were two or more boys, or more girls. It may be helpful if the children use counters of two colours to model the river crossing. They can record the results in the table on PCM 8, starting with 1 boy, 2 girls and 5 crossings.

Simplify

Ask them to keep the number of girls at 2 and then increase the number of boys. They need to look at the number of crossings needed to take over each boy: there is a pattern of four crossings needed to get one boy across. Draw a table of results without the column for the number of girls.

Challenge

Those children that can work algebraically should look for a formula for the number of crossings.

Number of boys (b)	Number of girls (g)	Number of crossings (c)
1	2	5
2	2	9
3	2	13
4	2	17

Number of crossings (with 2 girls) = 4b + 1.

Some children may express this verbally as 'the number of boys × 4 then +1 gives the number of crossings'.
What if there are more than 2 girls?

Checkpoints

 ### Watch out for ...

The table of results should help show the pattern for the generalization and so possibly a formula, but the diagram or picture illustrating the crossings will help show the pattern of four crossings for each additional boy. If children just see the number of crossings increasing by 4 each time, ask them to look at the relationship between the number of boys and the number of crossings.

 ### Ask ...

- ◗ *What do you notice ...?*
- ◗ *Is there a pattern in the way the numbers grow?*
- ◗ *Is there a relationship between the number of girls and the number of crossings?*

 ### Listen for ...

The children need to be systematic in the way they approach this problem, checking that they have found every possibility. Listen out for the way they work together, justifying their findings and supporting each other.

 Moving on ...

Ask the children to explain how they organized their results. Did any of them write an explanation of the patterns they found with the tables and diagrams? Ask the children if they could see any patterns between the number of girls and boys and the number of crossings. They may have used a table of results or found a rule by logical thinking. The last crossing always takes two girls. Each boy needs 2 crossings to get him over, so the number of additional crossings is $2(g - 2)$. If this is added to $4b + 1$ the formula becomes:

Number of crossings $(c) = 4b + 1 + 2 (g - 2)$
$$= 4b + 2g - 3$$

Where next?

- ◗ Try the 'chicken, fox and bag of corn' problem, crossing the river so that the fox isn't with the chicken and the chicken isn't with the corn. There are other puzzles to explore similar to this.
- ◗ Explore functions from function machines, presenting the results as graphs. Each number pair in the table of results can be represented as a pair of coordinates for a simple graph with numbered axes. The children can then explore the shapes of these graphs.

How well did the pairs support each other? Were their written notes and diagrams sufficiently clear for them to spot any patterns and how well could they explain any patterns they found? How could this idea of applying a systematic solution be developed?

DEBRIEF

One boy and two girls want to cross a river on a boat. The boat can only hold the following at any one time:

- one girl
- one boy
- two girls

How many crossings are needed to get everyone over?

Name _____ Date _____

What happens if ...

- ◑ there are two boys?
- ◑ there are three or more boys?
- ◑ there are more than two girls?

Number of boys	Number of girls	Number of crossings

Assessing progress

You know that children are developing their reasoning skills when they start using words like 'because', 'then' and 'so' in their discussions and their responses to your questions. They may also start to ask each other 'why?' questions and seek explanations from each other (and from you). Giving reasons as part of explanations then becomes a routine part of thinking lessons. Once you start to ask children why (or to ask another child why a response either was or was not correct) you will be able to assess the reasons in their responses. You need to ensure you ask children to justify correct and incorrect responses, otherwise they will 'read' your question as meaning they have made a mistake if you only ask 'why?' when an answer is wrong. Once children get used to this you can simply wait encouragingly or say 'because ...?' to get them to extend their replies to your questions to assess their reasoning skills.

Cross-curricular thinking

Science

Asking a question such as, *What will happen if?* is a good starting point for scientific reasoning. *What will happen if you put a tea cosy over an icy drink? Will it warm up faster or more slowly? What will happen if you drop a football and a cannonball from the top of a tall building? Will the cannonball reach the ground first?* Using thought provoking questions like these can stimulate scientific reasoning (as well as revealing children's thinking about scientific concepts).

History

A strategy like 'odd one out' can also be used to develop reasoning skills as the children are asked to give reasons for their choice of an 'odd one out' and can be encouraged to distinguish between historical and non-historical reasons. Choose three famous people and ask children to identify an odd one out with a historical reason.

Literacy

Justifying choices of words and phrases is a good way both to develop reasoning, and model thinking about composition. Asking a series of questions such as, *Why did you choose that adjective or powerful verb? What others did you consider? Why did you reject those?*, not only gives children the opportunity to give their reasons, but to make them explicit for others to hear.

Geography

Geographical enquiry is supported by reasoning as children express their views about places or changes to the environment. They can use a technique, such as identifying 'Plus, minus and interesting' points to compile a table, then justify the points they have identified with reasons.

Detective work

Enquiry skills

> **Enquiry** – these skills enable pupils to ask relevant questions, to pose and define problems, to plan what to do and how to carry out research, to predict outcomes and anticipate responses, to test conclusions and improve ideas. (QCA 2000)

Overview

Enquiry skills are as much a way of working or developing particular habits of mind which keep a range of possibilities open for as long as possible. The process of enquiry is about being flexible, looking for alternatives and testing a range of possible solutions. In mathematics these are essential skills as enquiry develops an understanding of relationships and connections that may not be immediately obvious.

The process of enquiry is at the heart of learning. It is only when you can identify what you need to know, go through a process of finding out and be able to recognize when you have found a solution that you can undertake independent learning. Enquiry skills can, therefore, best be developed in situations where it is not possible to see a solution from the outset and where children will benefit from working together.

There are good opportunities for speaking and listening in presenting the results of an investigation or enquiry. Enquiry lessons are also excellent for review and reflection about the process of learning.

The challenge for the teacher is at the beginning and end of the enquiry process. It is difficult to instruct children in how to ask relevant questions without directing them to a particular investigation or mathematical problem. Similarly, it is difficult enough for pupils to recognize that they have come up with a solution to an investigation, without them realizing that it is a good solution. Identifying what would be a better answer is even more difficult - challenging even for adults! Enquiry skills are also therefore, about developing more systematic habits of questioning as well as the specific skills in solving a problem.

Strategies

Enquiry skills can be broken down further into the following kinds of behaviours or activities that pupils can do:

- **Ask relevant questions**
  Enquire, be curious, ask, probe, investigate
- **Pose and define problems**
  Frame, propose, suggest, put forward an idea
- **Plan what to do and how to research**
  Think out, plan, sketch, formulate or organize ideas
- **Predict outcomes and anticipate responses**
  Suppose, predict, guess, estimate, approximate, foresee
- **Test conclusions and improve ideas**
  Experiment, test, improve, refine, revise, amend, perfect

Questions

Show me how you could …? What might work? What ideas have you got? What is a good question to ask? How could you find out? How could you check? Any predictions? What is your best guess? What are you expecting? About how much will it be?

The birthday present

BRiEF

In 'The birthday present' the children are presented with a letter outlining five ways to receive some money. The children need to make a decision about which scheme to choose and then explain the reasons for their decision. The children, in pairs or small groups, need to be encouraged to explore the possibilities and then put forward arguments in favour of a particular scheme.

Key maths links

- Problems involving money
- Properties of numbers and number sequences
- Making decisions

Thinking skills

- Enquiring and asking questions
- Organizing ideas
- Predicting outcomes
- Testing conclusions

Language

number sequences, spreadsheet, pattern, formula

Resources

PCM 9 (one per pair and/or enlarged)
PCM 10 (one per pair/ small group)

Setting the scene

Give out a copy of PCM 9 to each child or display the letter. Make sure that the children understand the five different options. Ask what predictions they have for the scheme and which ones they think would be the best to choose. *Which option looks best?* Before showing the children PCM 10, ask them how they think they will approach and organize the problem.

Getting started

Organize the class so that they work at the problem in pairs or small groups. For those children that need support in recording the results, give out PCM 10. Explain that the top chart can be used to record the amount that will be given for each year. The bottom chart can be used to keep a running total of the amounts each year. Make sure the children realize that they need to write a reply with reasons for their choice of scheme.

Simplify

Give a definite time, say 10 years. Running totals are quite a difficult idea for children to understand. If the children complete the top chart they can then draw 'loops' or colour in each cell to show when a particular amount has been added on. They will soon see that the years in the two charts correspond and each amount simply adds on to the previous year's total.

Challenge

Ask the children to present the results using a computer spreadsheet. They will find it easier to produce two spreadsheets, and PCM 10 can be used to show the basic structure.

Checkpoints

Watch out for ...

There could be confusion between running totals and totals for each year, particularly if they don't show the results in a table. Let the children discuss their ideas for organizing the information to see if they can think out a good approach to showing the results. There is no definite answer to this problem; it is up to the children to explore the range of possibilities and choose the scheme they would prefer.

Ask ...

- *How much easier would it be if you knew how many years the money was to be given?*
- *What if Great Aunt Sylvia lived until she was 100?*
- *Did your results match your prediction?*

Listen for ...

Some children will quickly realize that a table is a good way of organizing the results. They will be looking for patterns in the results and be able to make generalizations, perhaps with formulae to generate results.

 Moving on ...

Ask some of the groups of children to read out their letters. Find out the most popular scheme and talk about the reasons why this was the most popular. This table shows the results for 10 years:

Year	Scheme a	Scheme b	Scheme c	Scheme d	Scheme e
1	100	1	10	50	500
2	190	3	30	100	500
3	270	7	60	150	500
4	340	15	100	200	500
5	400	31	150	250	500
6	450	63	210	300	500
7	490	127	280	350	500
8	520	255	360	400	500
9	540	511	450	450	500
10	550	1023	550	500	500

Where next?

- The results of this task could be presented as a line graph so that the different schemes can be visually compared.
- Use spreadsheets to explore the area of different rectangles with the same perimeter.
- The children can use spreadsheets to run a small 'business' such as a tuck-shop. They need to use formulae so that any change in prices or numbers sold will be easily altered for all figures so that they can predict costs and potential profits.

How well did the children organize the information and then use it to inform their decision? Was there evidence of the children refining and amending their thoughts as the task developed? Could they reason with each other and present a 'case' for their preferred option? How could this idea of considering consequences over time be developed?

DEBRIEF

The birthday present

Read the letter from Great Aunt Sylvia.

1st

Mr Bernard Jeffries
36 Walnut Drive

Summerfield Cottage,
South Wadesby,
Norfolk

Dear Bernard,

Thank you for your lovely birthday card, it is hard to believe that I am now 70 years old!

You will be pleased to know that I have decided to give you some of my money. I shall give you an amount each year, starting now. You can choose which of the following schemes you would like to use.

a) £100 now, £90 next year, £80 the year after and so on.

b) £1 now, £2 next year, £4 the year after that, and so on.

c) £10 now, £20 next year, £30 the year after and so on.

d) £50 each year.

e) £500 now and no more in the future.

Of course the scheme can only operate while I am alive. I look forward to hearing which scheme you choose, and why!

Best wishes,

Great Aunt Sylvia

Totalling the birthday present

Name _____ Date _____

Which scheme should Bernard choose?

Totals each year

Year	Scheme a	Scheme b	Scheme c	Scheme d	Scheme e
1	£100	£1	£10	£50	£500
2					
3					
4					
5					
6					
7					
8					
9					
10					

Running total

Year	Scheme a	Scheme b	Scheme c	Scheme d	Scheme e
1	£100	£1	£10	£50	£500
2					
3					
4					
5					
6					
7					
8					
9					
10					

Thinking by Numbers 6 • **Unit 3: Detective work** • **Enquiry skills**

Giant feet

'Giant feet' starts with a simple problem for the children to solve about themselves: *How much space do you have in your shoe?* The children decide on a method for working this out. They use the information to investigate the size of a giant's foot. Throughout the activity the children will be expected to collaborate in small groups, deciding on appropriate methods, refining results and researching information so that they can justify their results. The level of accuracy of the results will vary from group to group. This task needs a high level of engagement so it is important to get the activity off to a good start and capture the children's enthusiasm.

Key maths links

- ◗ Measures – area
- ◗ Making decisions
- ◗ Problems involving measures

Thinking skills

- ◗ Enquiring and investigating possible outcomes
- ◗ Defining problems
- ◗ Testing and refining ideas

Language

measure, compare, area, length, square metre (m²), square centimetre (cm²)

Resources

PCM 11 (one per group)
PCM 12 (one per group)

 Setting the scene

Read the start of the second chapter 'Who?' from Roald Dahl's *The BFG*. The children are likely to have read the book when they were younger and this chapter sets the scene, including the line: 'It was four times as tall as the tallest human.' After a brief discussion about the book, explain that the class will be investigating and comparing a giant's feet and shoes with their own. Give out a copy of PCM 11 to each group of children or display it to the class. Read through the sheet, going over each of the three distinct parts of the activity. Ask them how they think they will approach the problem. Give them a few moments, in groups, to consider and plan how to organize their ideas. Explain that you want the results presented as a poster.

 Getting started

The children may decide to split their group up so pairs work on each of the three parts of the activity or they may work on each part together. They need to research the size of shoes of 'tall humans' and relate shoe sizes to length. The usual adult English shoe size scale ranges from size 1 to 12, with each size interval equal to $\frac{1}{3}$ inch or 8·4 mm. PCM 12 is a follow up activity, using the information gained from the first sheet.

Simplify

The giant's size could be changed to four times as big as an 11-year-old so that the children's measurements can be used to relate sizes. The area of feet and shoes can be measured in squares. If necessary, the bottom half of PCM 12 can be cut off and left out.

Challenge

The area of feet and shoes can be measured in square centimetres or square millimetres for more accuracy. The children could find out the shoe size of the tallest human so that the giant's foot and shoe size can be measured exactly. Ask how much space the giant would have in his shoe.

Checkpoints

Watch out for ...

Make sure the groups are working effectively early on. Compare ideas as a class at different stages, to check they are on track. Groups may find the recording difficult. Encourage them to record the results as a poster, with all the information presented inside their drawing of the giant's footprint.

Ask ...

- How could you find out ...?
- Is that as accurate as you can find?
- Any predictions? How big do you think his foot would be?

Listen for ...

Collaboration is important for this activity so listen out for the ways that the children relate to each other and share out the tasks. They should be thinking about ways of refining to make their results accurate. Highlight where (and how) the groups are working together well.

Moving on ...

Compare each of the completed posters. Are there many variations in the results? Ask if they can think why the results vary and discuss accurate measuring. For example, if two groups' findings for an adult foot length has a 2 cm difference, this will be increased to 8 cm for the giant. This is a difference of almost 10 shoe sizes! Talk about the ways the groups organized themselves. Did they feel that they worked well as a group?

Where next?

- Investigate shoe size measurements around the world. Standard scales include the US scale, the French scale and the Japanese scale.
- Investigate the relationship between length, area and volume of cubes and cuboids.
- Use *The BFG* by Roald Dahl as a starting point for creative writing, art and technology. Find the descriptions in the book of the BFG's feet and shoes and draw a picture of them. Papier mâché and wire models could be made of his shoes.

How well did the children collaborate and share out the tasks. Was there any evidence of them explaining their findings and reporting back to the group? Were the children able to refine and amend their thoughts as the task developed? How could you develop their collaborative skills further?

DEBRIEF

Name _____ **Date** _____

How much bigger is your shoe than your foot?

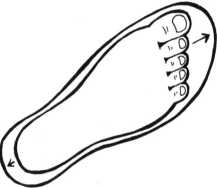

This huge giant is four times bigger than a tall human.

Draw a life-size picture of the giant's foot.

What shoe size would he need?

_____

Name _____ **Date** _____

How many children can fit in 1 m²? Would the giant fit in 1 m²?

Find out a little more about BFG's shoes...

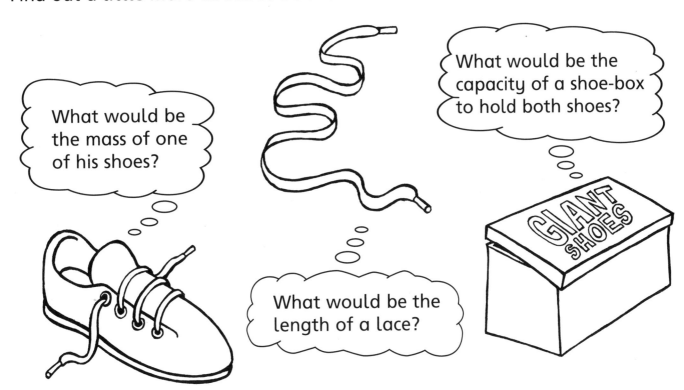

What would be the mass of one of his shoes?

What would be the length of a lace?

What would be the capacity of a shoe-box to hold both shoes?

GIANT SHOES

Assessing progress

Evidence that children are making progress in developing enquiry skills can be gained by observing the way that they are working. Enquiry is as much a habit, or an attitude, of keeping a range of possibilities open for as long as possible. Being flexible, looking for alternatives and testing a range of possible solutions are therefore good indications that enquiry skills are developing.

Cross-curricular thinking

Literacy

Another variation on the 'Living graphs' (page 22) strategy is developing the understanding of narratives, both in fiction and non-fiction texts (such as historical narratives), through discussion and enquiry. The graph is replaced with a 'fortune line' about a character's feelings or mood. The children place statements from the narrative on the graph. To do this they need to sequence the text and empathize with the character. Investigating a number of similar narratives (such as traditional tales) will show that they tend to have a similar shaped graph, reflecting the narrative structure and the use of repetition to develop suspense (in *The Three Billy Goats Gruff* and *Little Red Riding Hood*, for example).

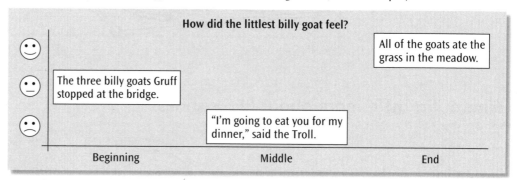

How did the littlest billy goat feel?

- All of the goats ate the grass in the meadow.
- The three billy goats Gruff stopped at the bridge.
- "I'm going to eat you for my dinner," said the Troll.

Beginning   Middle   End

History

Fortune lines can also be used in historical enquiry particularly to develop empathy, the statements can either come from real historical figures (the diaries of Samuel Pepys and Anne Frank are good sources) or characters created for the task (such as a child miner in Victorian times).

Science

Developing scientific enquiry means the children must think up questions that can be investigated. An approach called 'Philosophy for children' has been shown to encourage children to develop questioning skills. It uses a stimulus as a starting point, commonly a familiar story, but it can be a poem or a picture, that the children think up questions about. They then select one to answer in a class discussion called a 'community of enquiry'. It is possible to extend this into science where questions can be investigated and you can challenge the children to work out how they could find out the answer.

Geography

This approach can work in geography, particularly when a photograph of a stimulating environment or an interesting landscape is used as the starting point. After a discussion of what the children think, their motivation to find out is likely to be enhanced.

What if ...?
Creative thinking skills

> **Creative thinking** – these skills enable pupils to generate and extend ideas, to suggest hypotheses, to apply imagination and to look for alternative, innovative outcomes. (QCA 2000)

Overview

Creative thinking is the kind of thinking that produces new insights, approaches, or perspectives. It is essential in education that learners see that they can come up with new ideas or suggestions which help their own thinking as well as stimulating the thinking of others. No one expects a 7- or 11-year-old to come up with something unique in the history of human development, but unless we value the creativity that young children naturally have they will stop thinking creatively and rely on reproducing ideas they have been given by others.

Creativity is often *not* associated with mathematics in schools, but thinking up new solutions to problems, seeing new connections, or thinking of more efficient or effective alternatives is what mathematicians do. It is not necessary for the ideas to be completely original, just new for the individual pupil or shared with the class for the first time, or it might be that ideas or concepts are seen in a new or unusual way. It is important that pupils feel comfortable in order to be creative. They need to have confidence that their ideas will be accepted and that there is a range of possible answers or solutions to a problem or issue. The aim is to encourage pupils to think up a range of ideas, to have new thoughts or ideas (at least for them) or to extend and develop other people's ideas.

There are a number of techniques and approaches to support creative thinking such as brainstorming, thinking of analogies, visualizing or picturing possibilities. What all these techniques have in common is an emphasis on the flow of ideas. This means that in the early stages of supporting creative thinking it is essential to be uncritical to ensure that thinking is not too restricted.

Strategies

Creative thinking skills can be broken down further into the following kinds of behaviours or activities that pupils can do:
- **Generate and extend ideas**
  Brainstorm, think up, develop, extend
- **Suggest hypotheses**
  Suppose, surmise (*use phrases like 'how about ...?', 'it could be ...'*)
- **Apply imagination**
  Design, devise, visualize, elaborate
- **Look for alternative, innovative outcomes**
  Think laterally, fancy, guestimate, invent

Questions

Can you imagine? What would that look like? How could you change it to make it a ... ? Can you think of a question you could ask? Go on ... What will the answer look like? Another idea? And another ...

Washing machines

BRIEF

'Washing machines' involves the children in looking at the relationship between the number of programmes available with different washing machine models and the number of features they have. The children need to decide on a way of organizing and presenting their findings so that they can recognize any patterns in their results. This can then lead on to predicting the number of programmes from different combinations and generalizing for any number of options.

Key maths links

- ▶ Reasoning and generalizing about numbers
- ▶ Number sequences
- ▶ Solve mathematical problems and explain patterns and relationships

Thinking skills

- ▶ Generating and extending ideas
- ▶ Applying imagination
- ▶ Exploring alternative outcomes

Language

investigate, pattern, calculate, predict, rule, formula, relationship, factors

Resources

PCM 13 (one per pair and/or enlarged)
PCM 14 (one per pair)

 Setting the scene

Explain that you saw an advert for a new washing machine that boasted 1000 different programmes – more than enough for most types of washing! Spend some time brainstorming or mind-mapping the possible features that a washing machine might have. Give out or display PCM 13 and look at Model A. Explain that this is the basic model in a range of washing machines. Ask the children how many different possible programmes there are altogether. Discuss ways of tackling this problem. Ask them how they could show this in a diagram or chart. Repeat this for Model B. Review the different approaches and discuss which would be easy to extend if there were more options (for features or washing machines).

 Getting started

Ask the children to work in pairs and to look at Models C and D. You want them to investigate the number of possible programmes for each model, and to record this so that the results are clearly displayed. Ask them to think about other models. What if ...

- ▶ there were 4 temperatures and 3 spin speeds?
- ▶ there were 5 temperatures, 2 spin speeds and 2 rinses?

Can they find a quick way of calculating the answer for any model?

The children then need PCM 14 to design their own machines with an advanced range of features. They need to label their machines, listing the features. Ask them to work out the number of possible programmes for their machines.

Simplify

Give the children a different range of washing machines so that there are always 2 spin settings and an increasing number of temperature choices. The approach to solving the problem of the number of programmes is then much more systematic and more organized for the children.

Challenge

Ask the children to make one of their washing machine designs have 1000 possible programmes, like the advert. *What range and number of features can give exactly 1000 combinations?*

Checkpoints

Watch out for …

Some children may struggle to see any patterns. This table of results may help:

Model	Number of choices	Number of possible combinations
A	4 (2 + 2)	4 (2 × 2)
B	5 (3 + 2)	6 (3 × 2)
C	6 (4 + 2)	8 (4 × 2)
D	8 (4 + 2 + 2)	16 (4 × 2 × 2)

Ask …

- ◗ *How would an extra choice change the number of programmes?*
- ◗ *What do you notice with the results?*
- ◗ *Is there another design with the same number of programmes?*

Listen for …

The children need to be systematic in their recording. They may recognize pairs or combinations of factors. For example, they may discover that a machine with 3 spin speeds, 4 temperatures and 4 rinse options has the same number of programmes as a machine with 4 spin speeds, 6 temperatures and 2 rinse options.

Moving on …

Ask the children to explain how they organized their results and compared the possible number of programmes for different options. This can then be related to the factors of different numbers and prime factors can also be introduced. For example, the prime factors of 60 are 2, 2, 3 and 5. Did any of the children's washing machine designs use prime factors? What about a machine with 1000 programmes?

Where next?

- ◗ Design some advertising to go with their washing machines. This could include a poster and radio broadcasting.
- ◗ Use the same principle to design an ice-cream-making machine to make different combinations of flavours and toppings.
- ◗ Is more choice necessarily a useful thing? Look at machines such as microwaves, bread-makers and mixers. When there are a lot of choices how many are actually used? Carry out a survey and analyze the results.

How well did the brainstorming part of the activity work? Were the children able to come up with creative suggestions? How well did the pairs support each other? Were their notes and diagrams sufficiently clear for them to spot any patterns and how well could they explain their findings?

DEBRIEF

Washing machines

Name _____ **Date** _____

How many programmes are available with these models and their different options?

MODEL A

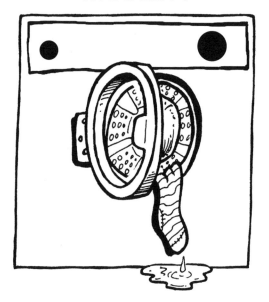

- ◐ hot or cold wash
- ◐ long or short spin

MODEL B

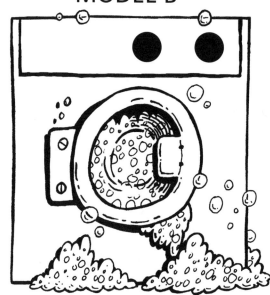

- ◐ 3 temperatures:
  cold, warm, hot
- ◐ long or short spin

MODEL C

- ◐ 4 temperatures:
  20°C, 40°C
  60°C, 80°C
- ◐ long or short spin

MODEL D

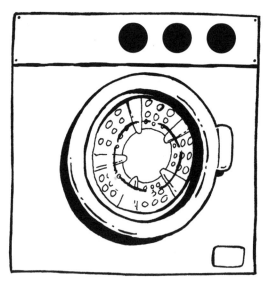

- ◐ 4 temperatures:
  20°C, 40°C
  60°C, 80°C
- ◐ long or short spin
- ◐ single or double rinse

Thinking by Numbers 6 • **Unit 4: What if …?** • **Creative thinking skills**

My washing machine models

Name _____ Date _____

Design and label two more washing machine models, with more features than the basic models. Features could include:

- ○ pre-wash
- ○ more rinse settings
- ○ delay start
- ○ tumble-drying
- ○ more temperatures

> How many programmes are possible with your machines?

Features:

Features:

Spiral paths

BRiEF

'Spiral paths' is an open-ended shape investigation. The starting point is a 90° spiral repeat of three lines, with the length of each line determining the shape and size of the spiral pattern. The children explore a range of different spirals and then compare the line lengths and shapes of each spiral. They need to be encouraged to be creative, imaginative and questioning in their approach, with a willingness to make and test conjectures. The depth and detail possible with this investigation will show the level of thinking being applied by the children.

Key maths links

- Reasoning and generalizing
- Shape and space – angles
- Measures – area and length

Thinking skills

- Generating and extending ideas
- Making and testing conjectures
- Applying imagination
- Exploring alternative outcomes

Language

angle, area, clockwise, predict, generalize, pattern

Resources

PCM 15 (one per pair and/or one enlarged)
PCM 16 (one per pair)
squared grid paper

 ## Setting the scene

Ask the children to visualize a spiral and describe it to a partner. Get them to sketch a spiral and give instructions as to how to draw it for their partner to follow. Next, demonstrate the rules for drawing a spiral, displaying an enlarged copy of PCM 15. Show that each turn is 90° clockwise and the three numbers show the lengths of each line in order. These lengths are repeated until the spiral is complete. Use a squared grid to show that a (3, 2, 1) spiral is the same size and shape as a (1, 3, 2) spiral. Ask the children to predict the shape of spirals with different length lines, and check that they realize that there are four repeats to make a closed spiral with three lengths.

 ## Getting started

Give out PCM 16 and some squared paper and ask the children to work in pairs or small groups to explore patterns made with spiral paths. To begin with, they explore a range of different spirals, looking for any similarities and differences. Encourage them to ask questions about their findings, for example, *Why does this spiral have a square in the middle and this one doesn't?* Once they have had time to explore, they then need to follow their own line of investigation. The ideas given in the 'investigate' section of the sheet give some starting points as examples.

Simplify

With the children, look at spirals made by repeating 1 length (a square), 2 lengths (a rectangle), 3 lengths (a closed spiral), 4 lengths (an open spiral) and so on. Then find out why some squares have a 'cross' at the centre and others have a square.

Challenge

Ask the children to investigate the area of each rectangle part, and the area enclosed by the spiral. They can find the relationship between the line lengths and the area.

Checkpoints

Watch out for ...

Make sure the children always draw the next line rotated 90˚ in the same clockwise direction.

Ask ...

- ❍ *How are they similar?*
- ❍ *How are they different?*
- ❍ *What if you changed the length of the shortest line?*

Listen for ...

Some children will be comparing different spiral paths in their groups and looking for similarities and differences. They may make conjectures, but it is the quality of the testing of these conjectures that will determine whether the children are able to generalize and explain their findings.

Moving on ...

Ask the children to explain how they organized and presented their results. Talk about open and closed spirals and the different 3-length spirals, with a cross and a square in the centre. The children should be able to explain that there is a 'cross' when two of the line lengths added together equal the longest length: $(a + b = c)$. If they are not equal then a square will be at the centre of a spiral. They may be able to generalize for the area of the square at the centre: the longest line, subtract the total of the other two lines, all squared: $[c - (a + b)]^2$. The area of each of the four rectangles within a spiral is a fairly simple formula: (ab), whereas the rule for the outside area of the square taken up by each shape is a more complicated generalization: $[(b + c) - a]^2$. Discuss these if appropriate.

Where next?

- ❍ What if the angle of turn is 60˚? Explore the spirals on triangular paper or isometric dotty paper.
- ❍ Use LOGO to explore spirals and test the generalizations by programming a roamer or screen turtle to draw out the spiral patterns. Alternatively LOGO could be the method used by groups of children to explore the different spirals.
- ❍ Spirals occur in nature, such as shells and plants, and can be investigated further.

Were the children able to give this investigation the creative thinking necessary to make it challenging? Were they questioning in their approach and able to make conjectures? What strategies did they use if they became stuck or reached a dead-end? How well could they explain any patterns they found and make generalizations?

DEBRIEF

Spiral paths

Name _____ **Date** _____

90° spiral patterns can be made by repeating lines of three lengths.

The turns are always 90° clockwise.

Here is how a (1, 3, 2) spiral path is made.

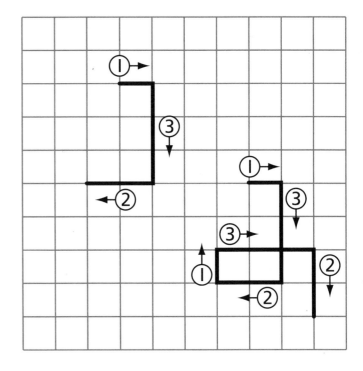

This is a completed (1, 3, 2) spiral path.

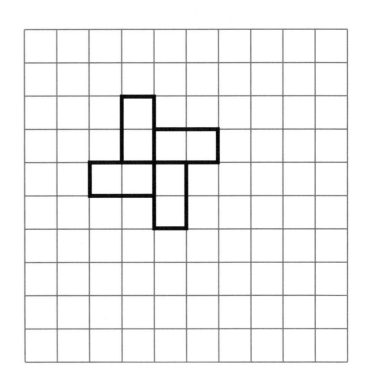

- ○ What would a (3, 2, 1) spiral look like?
- ○ How many repeats are needed to make a 'closed' shape?
- ○ Can you predict what a (2, 4, 6) spiral would look like?

More spiral paths

Name _____ Date _____

Explore the patterns made with different 90° spiral paths.

This is a (3, 4, 8) spiral path.

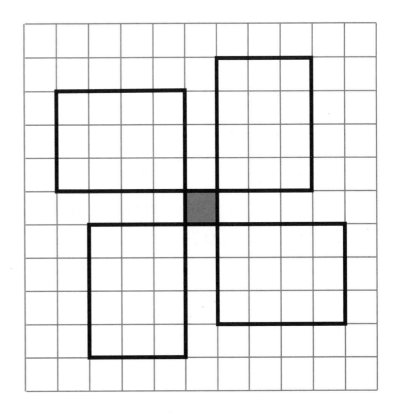

What if ...
- ○ two of the numbers are the same?
- ○ three of the numbers are the same?
- ○ the order of the numbers is changed?
- ○ more than three numbers are repeated?

Investigate ...
- ○ spirals that have similar shapes
- ○ spirals that have central squares
- ○ the area of each rectangle or square
- ○ the area enclosed by the whole shape.

Assessing progress

Assessing the development of creative thinking is challenging as there are often a number of solutions and ideas that can be considered creative in any particular situation. You will have to consider the individual pupil too. A genuinely creative thought for one pupil - something new and insightful for them - may not be so creative in another. Also the process is not necessarily regular or frequent. It is therefore important to consider children's attitudes or their dispositions in different situations. They should be asking questions and confident to offer ideas. It is this confidence or perhaps playfulness that is the best indicator of creativity, rather than trying to assess specific solutions or outcomes.

Cross-curricular thinking

Literacy

Brainstorming for ideas is a good general technique to develop creative thinking. It is important that it is done in an atmosphere where the children know that offering ideas is more important than coming up with the right answer and where all ideas are accepted uncritically. In literacy this technique can be used when responding to a text to record thoughts and feelings, as well as to stimulate ideas for composition in terms of the content and detail of the vocabulary used. Brainstorming is usually conducted as a whole class activity. It can also be useful to start off in groups so that the children become more independent in using the technique.

Science

Using analogies can be a powerful way to develop scientific understanding in a creative way. Asking children to think of an analogy for something (such as an electric current being like water pipes with the current flowing round a circuit) not only provides an opportunity to compare why they are alike and how they are not alike, but also offers an insight into children's thinking about the science involved.

Design Technology

Coming up with ideas is an essential part of the design process. One technique that can help is to ask children to visualize how the product will be used. Ask them to 'see' it once it is finished: *What will it need to do?, What will make your idea different or special?* This can be the basis for more structured planning and development, though the whole process is a creative one.

Geography

The strategy 'Banned' (see page 23) can easily be developed in other subjects and provides opportunities to develop specific vocabulary. However, it can also be a way to stimulate creative thinking as children will come up with imaginative ways to give clues to words, such as: *It sounds like fountain but starts with an 'm'.* They may find it hard to formulate rules for banned ideas or words. It is usually best to praise their ingenuity and finish with a discussion of creative ways to get round the rules.

In my opinion ...

Evaluation skills

> **Evaluation** – these skills enable pupils to evaluate information, to judge the value of what they read, hear and do, to develop criteria for judging the value of their own and others' work or ideas and to have confidence in their judgements. (QCA 2000)

Overview

Evaluation is about taking responsibility for your own opinions and judgements and being prepared to explain or defend them to others with reasons. It requires confidence in knowing what you think and sensitivity in evaluating or criticizing the work of others. It requires the ability to set and apply criteria to tasks and make judgements based on those criteria. The final stage is presenting these judgements to others and being prepared to defend or change that judgement in the light of feedback. This involves awareness of the feelings of others in giving and receiving feedback - a challenging aspect of effective collaboration and an important aspect of speaking and listening.

In mathematics evaluation is essential in developing confidence in knowing that you have a good solution and understanding why. Mathematics is often perceived as being about applying rules or being able to remember facts and formulas. However, an essential part of being able to think mathematically is to be able to make judgements about which facts to use or which formula to apply. A good solution in mathematics might be an efficient one, or an elegant one, or one that leads to new insights and thinking. Deciding which is the best way to do something mathematically therefore, often calls for evaluation and judgement.

Strategies

Evaluation skills can be broken down further into the following kinds of behaviours or activities that pupils can do:

- **Evaluate information**
  Appraise, assess, critique, decide
- **Judge the value of what they read, hear and do**
  Review, weigh up, scrutinize
- **Develop criteria for judging the value of their own and others' work or ideas**
  Evaluate, judge, mark
- **Being confident in their judgements**
  Express opinions, disagree, agree (with reasons), resolve

Questions

How could you justify that? What reasons are important? Can you explain ...? How will you check it? Can you argue the opposite? Do you agree? Do you disagree? Which do you think?

Holiday hot spots

BRIEF

'Holiday hot spots' gives a range of information about two seaside resorts. From the information the children choose a resort that would be best for certain groups of people and design an advertising leaflet for their chosen group. You need to encourage the children to be as informed as possible by using all the information given. This will include finding the average number of hours of sunshine and the average weekly temperature.

Key maths links

- ▶ Handling data – averages and interpreting graphs
- ▶ Making decisions
- ▶ Problems involving 'real life' and measures

Thinking skills

- ▶ Evaluating information
- ▶ Expressing opinions

Language

temperature, average, mean, median, mode, range, bar chart

Resources

PCM 17 (one per pair and/or one enlarged)
PCM 18 (one per pair)

 ### Setting the scene

Explain that the children will be working in pairs to compare two holiday resorts in order to choose a suitable resort for a week's holiday for different groups of people. Display PCM 17 and explain that this shows the temperatures and hours of sunshine for the previous week, and that they will be very similar for the week of the holiday. Read through the features of each resort and ask the children for their first impressions and general view of each resort.

 ### Getting started

Give out PCM 18 and ask the children to choose one of the groups. Explain that you want them to design a leaflet for this group giving as much information as possible, including temperatures and sunshine hours. Discuss the different forms of average - mode, median and mean, and talk about the range. Explain that this may help decide which would be the best resort for their group of people. The leaflet is a suggested design style but encourage the children to use a poster or flyer if they wish.

Simplify

Ask the children to use the high and low temperatures and sunshine hours rather than working out any averages.

If the children find it difficult to empathize with different groups they could choose the resort that they would prefer.

Challenge

The children can include comparison figures for the two resorts in their leaflet, highlighting averages that support their chosen resort. Talk about the way that statistics can be manipulated to alter the views of people reading the information.

Checkpoints

Watch out for ...

It would be easy to choose a resort and give very general reasons for the choice. Encourage the children to evaluate the information given and decide on strengths and weaknesses using these details. This can then be backed up by any statistics they feel supports their chosen resort. Check that the children know how to work out mean averages and know the difference between this type of average and the mode and median averages.

Ask ...

- ❍ *How could you justify your choice?*
- ❍ *Can you argue the opposite?*
- ❍ *Which information convinces you?*
- ❍ *Do you both agree?*

Listen for ...

The children will be trying to find strengths and weaknesses for each resort. They should be trying to justify their decisions and, by empathizing with the different groups, finding a resort that matches the needs of that group. Listen for the ways in which the two resorts are compared and the level of detail used. Are they able to manipulate the data to emphasize the strengths of their chosen resort?

Moving on ...

Display the different finished leaflets and ask each pair to explain the main reasons for their choice. Compare the results of children who chose the same groups. For example, did all the children who designed a leaflet for the young married couple choose Brightsea as their resort?

Where next?

- ❍ The children could research two different types of resort or holiday destination, such as two camp sites or two ski resorts. They find out as much information as they can, including costs, and produce a comparison of the resorts as a TV or radio broadcast.
- ❍ Temperatures and sunshine hours change from year to year. The children could research, record and display the changes over the last, say, 20 years, in their home town. Global warming, pollution and the ozone layer could be hot topics for debate.

How well did the children use the information to help advertise their chosen resort? Were they able to look at strengths and weaknesses and compare resorts through the eyes of the different groups? How did they use the statistics to support their arguments and were they able to justify their choice through argument and counter-argument?

DEBRIEF

Holiday hot spots

Read the information about the seaside resorts.

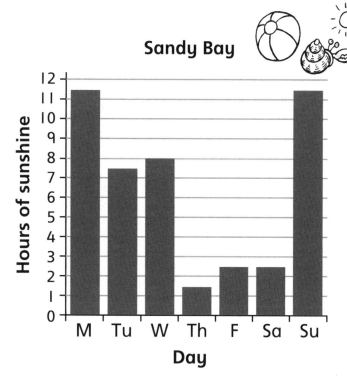

DAY	M	Tu	W	Th	F	Sa	Su
TEMP (°C)	28	25	27	20	21	20	27

DAY	M	Tu	W	Th	F	Sa	Su
TEMP (°C)	23	21	20	26	25	22	24

Tourist information: Sandy Bay

- range of cafés and restaurants
- plenty of free parking
- clean water award
- quiet resort
- safe swimming
- accommodation a short drive from beach
- a small park and boating lake

Tourist information: Brightsea

- entertainment each evening
- water sports available
- lively resort with pubs and a nightclub
- lifeguards on patrol
- clean, pebbly beach
- range of accommodation on seafront
- good local shops
- a small fairground

A holiday hot spot for you

Name _____ Date _____

Design a leaflet for the holiday resort that you think would be the best for one of these groups:

- a young married couple
- a group of over-60s
- a family with three children under 5 years old
- a family with two teenage children

My leaflet is for _____.

I think _____ holiday resort would best fit them

because _____

_____

_____

Birdwatching

BRIEF

'Birdwatching' is a thinking skills activity classified as a 'Mystery'. The children are given a real news report about a rare American Robin and then, using 18 pieces of information as clues, they decide whether a birdwatcher will have enough time to see the bird before it is, unfortunately, caught by a sparrowhawk. The activity challenges the children to make decisions about the relevance and importance of different pieces of information, and then use this information to work out a time line to show the birdwatcher's journey. Encourage collaboration and discussion, and observe the way that the groups organize the information and approach the problem.

Key maths links

- Problems involving 'real life' and measures
- Measures – time and distance

Thinking skills

- Interpreting information
- Speculating to form hypotheses
- Explaining and justifying

Language

kilometre, time, interpret, direction, journey, route, map

Resources

PCM 19 (one per group and/or one enlarged)
PCM 20 (one per group, with 18 clues cut out)
road maps
outline map of UK

 Setting the scene

Display PCM 19 so that the class can read the news headline together. Explain that this was a real event that happened in Lincolnshire in March 2004. Discuss the style of the report and clear up any misunderstandings or words that are difficult to understand. The use of the word 'rare' in the headline may need to be discussed and explain that a twitcher is a colloquial term for a birdwatcher. Point out that birdwatchers travelled long distances to see this rare bird. Explain that the class will be given clues about a birdwatcher, Tony, and his journey to Grimsby. The problem is – does he see the American robin before the sparrowhawk gets to it?

 Getting started

Put the children in groups of 4–6 and give each group a set of the clues. Explain that each group needs to decide how to use all the information to work out Tony's journey and the time it will take. They are trying to work out Tony's day in as much detail as possible. Some of the clues may be less important and some will have a major effect on the time taken. Explain that the cards can be moved around, grouped and sorted in whatever way the group wishes – collaboration is essential. Point out that there is no definite correct answer to this – it depends on the quality of their findings.

Simplify

Sort out the clues so that less important ones are put to one side and the 'time' clues are put in an order. Draw a time line for the group so that the journey can be roughly sketched out.

Challenge

Ask the children to show Tony's journey on a time/distance graph and then compare this to the route with times shown on a map.

③ Checkpoints

Watch out for ...

The early discussions within each group are crucial to the success of this, so that the children are motivated to develop and complete the task. Time/distance calculations can be tricky, so assign somebody in each group as a 'double-checker' using a calculator to check results.

Ask ...

- ❍ *Which are the important clues?*
- ❍ *Why do you think this is the best route?*
- ❍ *How certain are you that this is correct?*

Listen for ...

The children should be able to argue, discuss and listen without it getting too heated! Listen out for the way the clues are categorized and sorted.

④ Moving on ...

Talk about the clues and which ones were important facts, those that were opinions and those that were unimportant. Ask each group to present their findings and explain their solution to the class.

Where next?

- ❍ This type of 'Mystery' activity could be repeated with a different starting point and 15–20 clues. Time/distance problems work well, perhaps with the context of a family trying to get to an airport on time before a holiday. The packing and journey to the airport scene from the film *Home Alone* could be shown as a stimulus.
- ❍ The news article and Tony's journey could be combined to create a stimulus for a piece of creative writing.
- ❍ The children could find out about the work of the RSPB. What is their view of the incident with the American robin and the sparrowhawk?

How well did you manage the groups during the task so that strategies and methods could be shared if necessary? Did you bring the class together for small plenaries to share ideas? How well were you able to evaluate the thinking processes of the children within each group?

DEBRIEF

Read the newspaper article.

Tuesday, 9th March, 2004

The News

Twitchers watch robin served rare

Birdwatchers from all over Britain who gathered in Grimsby to catch sight of a rare American robin were horrified to see it eaten by a passing sparrowhawk.

They were still setting up their cameras when the predator swooped down from a row of drab factories and warehouses on an industrial estate.

The young bird, from the southern US, "didn't really live to enjoy her moment of fame," a twitcher told our journalist.

The robin's vivid red breast made it an obvious candidate for a lunch treat.

"It was a terrible moment," Graham Appleton, of the British Trust for Ornithology, which had spread news of the bird's arrival, told the newspaper.

Long-distance travels

But the trust's migration watch organizer, Dawn Balmer, was more philosophical. "Most of these rare visitors eventually succumb, anyway, to cold weather or a lack of food, if not predation," she told the paper.

The robin, whose scientific name *Turdus migratorius* derives from its long-distance travels within America, was probably blown across the Atlantic after being "caught up in a jetstream", Mr Appleton added.

AMERICAN ROBIN
Scientific name: *Turdus migratorius*
Average size: 21·5 cm
Lives: North America
Eats: insects, fruit, worms

A member of the thrush family, with oily-black wings and tail, the American robin is as big as a British blackbird.

Will Tony see the American robin before it is too late?

Tony has never seen an American robin.	Tony lives in Southampton, which is 415 km from Grimsby.	The sparrowhawk is spotted over Grimsby at 2:45 p.m.
The country roads in Lincolnshire are very quiet, winding and narrow.	The M25 has long traffic jams, with speeds reduced to 40 km/h in both directions. He drives for about 40 km on the M25.	After every 1 hour 30 minutes of driving Tony stops for a rest, food or petrol.
Each stop takes about 20 minutes.	He takes 10 minutes to pack cameras and binoculars.	The roads going north have no serious traffic problems.
He takes 30 minutes to shower and have breakfast before leaving.	Tony gets lost in Grimsby and takes 35 minutes to find the correct industrial estate.	The sparrowhawk sees the robin easily and quickly because of its bright red colouring.
Tony is a good driver and doesn't like to break speed limits!	The M3 is busy but moving freely.	Tony prefers minor roads to motorways, but speed is the priority.
Tony agrees to pick up his friend in Lincoln to take him to Grimsby. This adds 35 km to his journey.	On Tuesday 9th March Tony is woken at 6:15 a.m. by an urgent phone call from a friend who has seen the robin.	He only spends 15 minutes in Lincoln before setting off again.

Assessing progress

The children's increased confidence in their own thinking is one of the hallmarks of improving evaluation skills. It is about taking responsibility for your own opinions and judgements and being prepared to explain or defend them to others with reasons. This requires confidence in knowing what you think. This confidence should be justified, of course, so children should be prepared to change their minds if necessary, in the light of information or reasoning. At this stage it is also important for children to show sensitivity in evaluating or criticizing the work of others.

Cross-curricular thinking

Literacy

Assessment for learning (see page 14) strategies such as 'Traffic lights' are good starting points to develop evaluation skills. You can ask the children to rate a piece of writing that they have done with green for: *I think I can go on*, orange for: *I think I am getting going*, and red for: *I'm at a full stop here*. This opens up the way to discuss criteria for success in the task so that children can evaluate their own work.

Design technology

Evaluation is also central to design technology. The children need to learn to develop evaluation criteria for their designs in order to guide their thinking as they work. This should be an integral part of the process and not simply a retrospective review. Using a digital camera to record the process of designing and making enables the children to recall what they were thinking at the different stages and reflect on the criteria to evaluate the task.

History

A strategy such as a 'Mystery' (where snippets of information are pieced together to answer a central question) can help children to use their evaluative skills as they judge the importance of the different 'clues' they have been given. In history this can be a good way to assess understanding of what has been learned in a unit of work as they use their historical knowledge to do this. Clues can easily be written to support a discussion about: *Who was responsible for the Great Fire of London?* for example, to get children to see that the baker may have started the fire, but that there are other factors to consider.

Geography

Some other general techniques that are helpful in developing evaluation skills are those developed by Edward deBono where children are given thinking frames with headings such as 'Plus, minus and interesting' (PMI) (see page 23) or a focus on 'Consider all factors' (CAF). The structure of the sheet helps children to think more carefully and give more considered repsonses. These approaches can be combined with collaborative discussion (such as 'Think, Ink, Pair, Share' where children are asked to consider their response, make some notes, discuss it with a partner then in a group). This can be particularly useful in a subject like geography when the children have to evaluate changes to the environment or express their views about people and places.

Think on!

Using and applying thinking skills

> **Using and applying thinking** – in mathematics these skills involve pupils in developing the skills and strategies that will help them solve problems they face both in learning at school and in life more broadly. They involve problem solving in its broadest sense and include the skills of identifying and understanding what the issue or the problem is, planning solutions, monitoring progress in tackling the issue or problem and then reviewing and evaluating any solutions.

Overview

The aim of this unit is to identify some activities for pupils to put their mathematical thinking skills into practice. This will give them the opportunity to evaluate how well they have developed their skills through the earlier activities as well as giving you the opportunity to assess how well they can apply what they have learned. The activities are set as challenges, problems or puzzles.

The process of undertaking these activities relates to the different kinds of thinking in the earlier units. The early stages draw on information processing skills by focusing the children on what they have to do and what they already know. There may be scope for creativity in seeing alternatives or applying knowledge and skills imaginatively to a new problem. Enquiry skills are brought into play during the main part of the activity as any solution is formulated and tested, closely supported by reasoning skills which also help to link the different stages and ensure continuity throughout the process. Evaluation skills are essential to appraise and review any solution and to develop confidence in being successful.

Strategies

Supporting the pupils in using and applying thinking skills to problems is best framed as a series of questions:

- **What do we have to do?**
  What is the problem, challenge or issue to be resolved?
- **Where do we start?**
  What do we know?
  Have we done anything like this before?
  What possibilities are there?
- **How will we know when we have got there?**
  What will a successful solution look like?
- **Are we on track?**
  Is this going to lead us to the answer we imagined?
- **Have we got there?**
  Is this a solution to the problem we were set?
  Could we have done it differently? Is it the best solution?

Questions

What do you have to do? What do you need to know? What do you know already? Have you seen anything like this before? What could you try? Do you think that will work? What will the answer look like? How could you test that? How can you check that? Is this the best answer? How else could you have done it?

Discs

BRIEF

'Discs' involves tossing a pair of discs numbered on both sides. The totals that can be made are given and the children need to work out the numbers on the back of the discs. One possible approach is to model the discs and use trial and improvement to generate the correct totals. The children need to be encouraged to think of strategies for narrowing down the range of possible numbers. One of the aims of the activity is to get the children to think about the skills they have developed in the earlier activities.

Key maths links

- Properties of numbers and number sequences
- Reasoning about numbers

Thinking skills

- Problem solving
- Looking for alternative solutions
- Predicting outcomes and testing conclusions

Language

consecutive, total, sum, predict, trial and improvement

Resources

PCM 21 (one per pair and/or one enlarged)
PCM 22 (one per pair)
blank card circles

Setting the scene

Review some of the *Thinking by Numbers* tasks the class have done. Remind them of some of the skills and strategies that they have used and explain that the purpose of this task is for them to put these skills to good use! Make sets of card circles and write the numbers 6 and 4 on the fronts of a pair of them. Display the top half of PCM 21 and explain that you have these two discs with no numbers written on the back. Toss the discs to demonstrate and read the problem out. Brainstorm the methods they could use to find a solution. Trial and improvement may be suggested, so ask for some possible numbers to go on the back of the discs. Model the suggestions until the correct numbers are given (2 on the back of 6 and 9 on the back of 4).

Repeat this activity with the bottom part of PCM 21. Ask the children to work in pairs to try to work out the pairs of numbers. Talk about any strategies they used and demonstrate with a pair of discs to model the solution: disc one is 3 and 8, disc two is 2 and 5.

Getting started

Give PCM 22 and three card discs to pairs of children. The set of consecutive numbers from 11 to 16 are all the possible totals using these three discs. Ask them to use whichever method they wish, remembering what they have learnt from using two discs. Once they have solved the problem, they investigate other sets of three discs that make consecutive totals.

Simplify

Limit the activity by asking the children to explore two discs. Can they find a way of making consecutive totals with two discs? For example, disc one with 2 and 3, and disc two with 1 and 3, gives the totals 3, 4, 5 and 6. As support, explain that the largest and smallest totals that can be made are useful guides to the numbers on each disc.

Challenge

Ask the children to investigate the rules and patterns in making different totals. *What is the largest set of consecutive numbers that can be made? What if you had four discs?*

③ Checkpoints

Watch out for ...

Trial and improvement can be an unsatisfactory method if it is approached in a random, haphazard way. Encourage the children to be systematic in the choice of numbers, keeping a record of all the results to inform their next estimate.

Ask ...

- ❍ *What do you need to do?*
- ❍ *How can you check that?*
- ❍ *Is there a way to work systematically?*

Listen for ...

The children should cooperate in pairs, trying number combinations and checking solutions. Listen out for them using 'what if ...?' as a phrase to try different numbers. They may look for simple rules that help narrow down the range of numbers.

④ Moving on ...

Talk about the methods children used to work out the numbers on the back of the three discs at the top of PCM 22. The numbers are: 5 and 3, 2 and 4, 7 and 6. Discuss trial and improvement as a method. Did anybody find a systematic method for finding the numbers?

Where next?

- ❍ Consecutive numbers are good to explore. Ask the children to investigate sums of 2, 3, 4 ... consecutive numbers and develop this to investigate the sums of consecutive odd and even numbers.
- ❍ Tossing two discs can generate four totals. How many totals are possible with 3, 4, 5 ... discs?

Did the children develop any strategies or did they simply use random trial and improvement? Did they learn anything from using two discs that informed their approach to finding totals with three discs? Did you see any evidence of them using and applying the skills from earlier activities?

DEBRIEF

Two discs

Name _____ **Date** _____

These two discs have a number on each side.

When they are tossed, the totals that can be made when they land are:

10   6   11   15

> What are the numbers on the back of the discs?

These two discs have a number on each side.

When they are tossed, the totals that can be made when they land are:

10   8   13   5

> What are the four numbers on the discs?

Name _____ **Date** _____

These three discs have a number on each side.

When they are tossed, the different totals that can be made when they land are a set of consecutive numbers:

11   12   13   14   15   16

2

5

7

> What are the numbers on the back of the discs?

Make three discs with numbers on both sides.

Can you find numbers that make a set of consecutive totals?

Workings

Day trip to the beach

BRIEF

'Day trip to the beach' is an open-ended problem-solving task, involving decision-making by the children in pairs. Review some of the earlier activities that they have done and explain that this task is a chance for them to use these skills. They should use the information presented on the sheets to inform their judgements and help them work out a good day on the beach for two children, Dan and Lucy. The information shows times and prices for different items and events, presented as a series of posters and notices. The children need to organize and evaluate this information, assimilating it as a time line for Dan and Lucy's day.

Key maths links

- Making decisions
- Problems involving time and money

Thinking skills

- Solving problems
- Evaluating information
- Making judgements and decisions informed by evidence

Language

money, cost, estimate, 24-hour clock, timetable, time line, calculate

Resources

PCM 23 (one per pair)
PCM 24 (one per pair)

Setting the scene

Give out PCM 23 and go through the activity together. Explain that Dan and Lucy are on a coach trip to the beach with their family. They are given £10 each to spend, and have a variety of activities to choose from. Point out the coach ticket with arrival and departure times and also the time for lunch. Explain that they will be working in pairs to plan the day for the two children.

Getting started

Ask the children what other information is needed. They should come up with the fact that we don't know much about the children which makes it difficult to work out what they would enjoy. Give out PCM 24 and go through the short list about both children. This should help inform the judgements, but explain that there is no set solution. Each pair works out a plan for the day, making sure that no more than £10 is spent.

Simplify

Rather than planning a day for Dan and Lucy, the pairs could work out a day at the beach for themselves. They then simply need to think of the things that they would enjoy, whilst still working out the time and the costs involved with the activities.

Challenge

More activities could be included, so that there is a wider selection of times and prices. This could include mini-golf, bouncy castle, funfair rides etc. The pairs then need to make the day as active and full as possible with a £20 limit. You could get them to add a fortune line or mood graph to the task to evaluate if the money is well spent!

Checkpoints

Watch out for ...

Some of the times are in 24-hour and some in 12-hour time, so the children may need a little support if they struggle with this. The recording of times and amounts spent may be a little tricky to organize. PCM 24 gives one way of recording the time line, but the children may wish to sort it out in a different way.

Ask ...

- ❍ *Have you used all the information?*
- ❍ *Why do you think this is the best solution?*
- ❍ *Could you alter it to improve it?*

Listen for ...

The children may need to work out a rough timetable first and then refine it. They need to be able to empathize with Dan and Lucy and plan a suitable and enjoyable day for each, so expect children to argue and justify their choices and decisions.

Moving on ...

Ask pairs to compare their time lines and costs. Are any similar, or do the results vary? Talk about the activities chosen for each child and listen to pairs justifying their decisions. Check the accuracy and quality of the presentation of the results.

Where next?

- ❍ Use holiday brochures to plan a day trip or holiday. Give a budget and time constraints and compare the resulting choices.
- ❍ Ask the children to record a day at the weekend as a time line. Use the information to carry out a survey and present findings using graphs and charts. *What percentage of time is spent eating? What fraction of your day do you watch TV?*
- ❍ You could combine this chart with a mood graph and get children to discuss the cost effectiveness of their spending!

How did the children approach the problem? Were they careful and well organized, using the information to inform their decisions? Did they work well together, helping each other to sort out the information? Were they regularly evaluating their results and altering and refining the day so that it improved, or were they satisfied with their first attempts? Was there evidence of them using and applying skills from earlier activities?

DEBRIEF

Dan and Lucy are visiting the beach for the day with their family.

COACH TRIP: DAY TICKET TO BEACH

ARRIVE: 9:30 a.m. DEPART: 5:15 p.m.

LUNCH: 1:00–1:40 p.m.

THE SNACK SHACK

Candy-floss	90p
Ice-cream	75p
Ice lollies	55p
Doughnuts	£1·20
Bag of sweets	50p

BEACH EVENTS

TRAMPOLINING	10:30am	(1 hour)
SANDCASTLE COMPETITION	10:45am	(1 hour)
SCAVENGER HUNT	2:20pm	(50 mins)
VOLLEYBALL	3:30pm	(1 hour)
ROCK POOL STUDY	4:15pm	(55 mins)
ALL BEACH EVENTS £1·50		

Boat Trips: £1·75 each

DEPART	RETURN
09:35	10:20
10:55	11:35
11:55	12:40
12:50	13:55
14:15	14:50
15:10	15:55
16:10	17:00

PONY RIDES: £2 a go

Open 09:30 'til 16:30

Times: 09:40, 10:10, 10:40, 11:10...

and at the same time past each hour

Counting the cost of the trip

Name _____ **Date** _____

Dan and Lucy each have £10 to spend at the beach. Plan their day so that they spend the money … don't forget to allow time for swimming, playing and resting.

Dan, aged 12, likes:

sport
food
swimming
resting!

Lucy, aged 10, likes:

animals
playing in the sand
exploring
swimming

Dan	Activity	Cost
9:30		
10:00		
10:30		
11:00		
11:30		
12:00		
12:30		
1:00		
1:30		
2:00		
2:30		
3:00		
3:30		
4:00		
4:30		
5:00		
5:30		

Lucy	Activity	Cost
9:30		
10:00		
10:30		
11:00		
11:30		
12:00		
12:30		
1:00		
1:30		
2:00		
2:30		
3:00		
3:30		
4:00		
4:30		
5:00		
5:30		

Radio waves

BRiEF

'Radio waves' is a classic maths investigation with a simple starting point that can develop in different ways. The children, in pairs, are asked to connect rows of houses to two masts with straight lines and then count the number of 'cross-overs' or intersections. Through modelling by drawing diagrams, the children should use tables of results to generate sequences. Encourage the children to look for patterns in the results and generalize, either as a rule that can be described or as a formula.

Key maths links

- Properties of numbers and number sequences
- Reasoning and generalizing about numbers

Thinking skills

- Enquiring and asking relevant questions
- Making and testing conjectures
- Predicting outcomes
- Suggesting hypotheses

Language

pattern, sequences, generalize, intersection, rule, predict, relationship

Resources

PCM 25 (one per pair and/or one enlarged)
PCM 26 (one per pair)

Setting the scene

Display PCM 25 or give out one sheet per pair. Review some of the earlier strategies and tasks. Ask which activities might help them here. Talk about the examples with 2 and 3 houses built. This can be modelled with boxes to represent the houses and masts, and lengths of string to show the radio waves. Talk about the difficulties with increasing the number of houses. If they are all too close the intersections are difficult to see, and the patterns are more obvious if the houses are evenly spaced. Ask the children to predict the number of cross-overs they think there would be with 4 houses. (6 cross-overs)

Getting started

Give out PCM 26 to each pair. This asks them to find the number of cross-overs for 10 houses. Check that they have understood this problem before moving on to the next where they are asked to find the number of houses that can be built if the maximum number is 100 cross-overs. Explain that you want them to record the processes they go through before reaching any conclusions, writing down their thoughts, actions and ideas. Ask for suggestions as to how to record what they do.

Simplify

Ask the children to describe simply the patterns and the ways the numbers increase. They may see that with each house the numbers increase by 1 more than the previous number. They can then try to find the number of cross-overs for 6 houses and draw a diagram to show this.

Challenge

Ask the children to find an algebraic formula for the numbers generated. They need to see the relationship between the number of houses (n) and the number of intersections. This can be represented as: $n(n-1) \div 2$.

Checkpoints

Gather the class together to discuss progress. Invite a few pairs to show their methods of recording. *Have you been making predictions? Are they true/correct?*

Watch out for ...

Some children may struggle to find a generalization for *n* number of houses if they don't look at the relationship between the number of houses and the number of intersections, rather than simply describing the pattern of numbers of each column growing. Work on functions and function machines before this activity would help.

Ask ...

- ◗ *Can you see any patterns?*
- ◗ *What is the relationship between the numbers?*
- ◗ *Have you seen this set of numbers before?*
- ◗ *What do you think will be the next number?*
- ◗ *How could you test that?*

Listen for ...

The children will be trying to spot patterns in their results and may make conjectures. Listen out for the way they test these conjectures and whether the children are able to generalize and explain their findings. The children should be predicting the next number in the sequence and then finding a rule for any number of houses. Encourage them to try different methods and not to worry about making errors, they can learn from their mistakes.

 Moving on ...

Ask the children to explain how they organized and presented their results. Ask if they have seen this set of numbers before (the set of triangular numbers) and in what context. Any children that found the formula $n(n-1) \div 2$ can try to explain this to the rest of the class. Using this formula the maximum number of houses with less than 100 intersections would be 14 houses (91 intersections). Talk about the processes they went through and list them on the board. This could include: being systematic, looking for patterns, using diagrams, organizing results, making predictions, arguing, debating, listening, finding rules, generalizing ...

Where next?

- ◗ What if there were three radio masts that needed to connect to each house?
- ◗ What if the houses were built in a circle around a pair of radio masts?
- ◗ Investigate triangular numbers. *Where else do you see this set of numbers? What is their relationship with square numbers?*
- ◗ Use the list of processes to help the children as prompts if they get stuck on any future investigations.

Look at the list of processes and consider which of them are well developed in the way the children approach mathematical investigations. Were they questioning in their approach and able to make conjectures? What strategies did they use if they became stuck or reached a dead-end? Were their written notes and diagrams sufficiently clear for them to spot any patterns and how well could they explain any patterns they found and make generalizations?

DEBRIEF

Name _____ **Date** _____

Two radio masts are put up for a row of new houses. Each house is connected to both masts and radio waves travel in straight lines.

When 2 houses were built, there was 1 radio wave cross-over.

2 houses → ● = 1

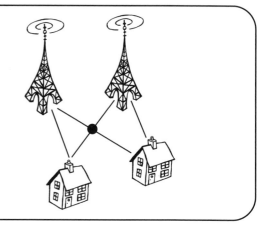

When 3 houses were built, there were 3 radio wave cross-overs.

3 houses → ● = 3

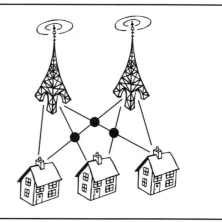

How many cross-overs are there for 4 houses?

Radio wave cross-overs

Name _____ **Date** _____

Two radio masts are put up, with each one connected to a row of new houses.

When 3 houses were built, there were 3 radio wave cross-overs.

3 houses → ● = 3

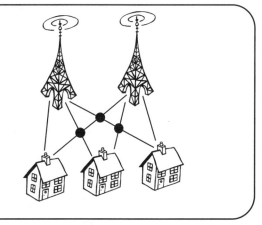

○ How many cross-overs are there when 10 houses are built?

○ How many houses can be built if the maximum number of cross-overs is 100?

Number of houses	Number of cross-overs
2	1
3	3
4	

Assessing progress

The aim of this final unit was to offer some activities for pupils to put their mathematical thinking skills into practice. This should have given you the opportunity to evaluate how well they have developed their skills through the earlier activities as well as the opportunity to assess how well they can apply what they have learned. The grid below is a way for you to review where you think the children have made progress. It is designed for you to use on the whole class, but could be used to reflect on individual children. It is set out as a grid so that you can indicate where you think the first five units were successful, whether the children were able to show these skills in the activities in Unit 6, where you think you have seen progress in other areas of the curriculum, and where you think the children have developed their awareness of their thinking skills. You may wish to review the activities with a colleague who has also been using the *Thinking by Numbers* activities.

Thinking skills		Units 1–5	Unit 6, Using and applying	Across the curriculum	Awareness of the skills
Information processing	locate and collect relevant information				
	sort				
	classify				
	sequence				
	compare and contrast				
	analyse part/whole relationships				
Reasoning	give reasons for opinions and actions				
	draw inferences				
	make deductions				
	use precise language to explain what they think				
	make judgements and decisions informed by reasons or evidence				
Enquiry	ask relevant questions				
	pose and define problems				
	plan what to do and how to research				
	predict outcomes and anticipate consequences				
	test conclusions				
	improve ideas				
Creative thinking	generate and extend ideas				
	suggest hypotheses, to apply imagination				
	look for alternative innovative outcomes				
Evaluation	evaluate information				
	judge the value of what they read, hear and do				
	develop criteria for judging the value of their own and others' work or ideas				
	have confidence in their judgements				

Appendix

Scope and sequence chart

Unit	Unit name	Activity name	Key maths links	Thinking skills	Page no.
1	Sort it out! *Information processing skills*	The matrix	● Properties of numbers ● Reasoning about numbers	● Information processing ● Working with patterns and rules ● Reasoning	26–29
		Cake stall	● Problems involving time and money ● Handling data – tables and charts	● Information processing ● Ordering and sequencing ● Reasoning	30–33
2	That's because ... *Reasoning skills*	Mood graphs	● Measures – time ● Handling data – line graphs	● Reasoning ● Drawing inferences and making deductions ● Make judgements informed by evidence	36–39
		Crossing the river	● Reasoning about numbers ● Generalization and formulae	● Reasoning and making deductions ● Logical thinking	40–43
3	Detective work *Enquiry skills*	The birthday present	● Problems involving money ● Properties of numbers and number sequences ● Making decisions	● Enquiring and asking questions ● Organizing ideas ● Predicting outcomes ● Testing conclusions	46–49
		Giant feet	● Measures – area ● Making decisions ● Problems involving measures	● Enquiring and investigating possible outcomes ● Defining problems ● Testing and refining ideas	50–53
4	What if ...? *Creative thinking skills*	Washing machines	● Reasoning and generalizing about numbers ● Number sequences ● Solve mathematical problems and explain patterns and relationships	● Generating and extending ideas ● Applying imagination ● Exploring alternative outcomes	56–59
		Spiral paths	● Reasoning and generalizing ● Shape and space – angles ● Measures – area and length	● Generating and extending ideas ● Making and testing conjectures ● Applying imagination ● Exploring alternative outcomes	60–63
5	In my opinion ... *Evaluation skills*	Holiday hot spots	● Handling data – averages and interpreting graphs ● Making decisions ● Problems involving 'real life' and measures	● Evaluating information ● Expressing opinions	66–69
		Birdwatching	● Problems involving 'real life' and measures ● Measures – time and distance	● Interpreting information ● Speculating to form hypotheses ● Explaining and justifying	70–73
6	Think on! *Using and applying thinking skills*	Discs	● Properties of numbers and number sequences ● Reasoning about numbers	● Problem solving ● Looking for alternative solutions ● Predicting outcomes and testing conclusions	76–79
		Day trip to the beach	● Making decisions ● Problems involving time and money	● Solving problems ● Evaluating information ● Making judgements and decisions informed by evidence	80–83
		Radio waves	● Properties of numbers and number sequences ● Reasoning and generalizing about numbers	● Enquiring and asking relevant questions ● Making and testing conjectures ● Predicting outcomes ● Suggesting hypotheses	84–87

Thinking by Numbers 6 and the NNS Unit Plans

The following chart shows how the thinking activities could be used if following the teaching order suggested in the NNS Unit Plans. Choose an appropriate activity to suit your class.

Autumn Term				
		Thinking by Numbers		
Unit	Unit topic	Activity name	Thinking skill	Page no.
1	Place value	Unit 3: Giant feet	Enquiry	50–53
2	Multiplication and division, mental methods	Unit 3: The birthday present	Enquiry	46–49
		Unit 4: Washing machines	Creative thinking	56–59
		Unit 4: Spiral paths	Creative thinking	60–63
		Unit 5: Holiday hot spots	Evaluation	66–69
		Unit 5: Birdwatching	Evaluation	70–73
		Unit 6: Day trip to the beach	Using and applying	80–83
		Unit 6: Radio waves	Using and applying	84–87
3	Multiplication and division, written methods	Unit 3: The birthday present	Enquiry	46–49
		Unit 3: Giant feet	Enquiry	50–53
		Unit 5: Holiday hot spots	Evaluation	66–69
		Unit 5: Birdwatching	Evaluation	70–73
		Unit 6: Day trip to the beach	Using and applying	80–83
4	Fractions, decimals and percentages	Unit 3: Giant feet	Enquiry	50–53
		Unit 5: Holiday hot spots	Evaluation	66–69
5	Fractions, decimals and percentages, ratio and proportion	Unit 3: Giant feet	Enquiry	50–53
		Unit 5: Holiday hot spots	Evaluation	66–69
6a	Handling data	Unit 1: Cake stall	Information processing	30–33
		Unit 2: Mood graphs	Reasoning	36–39
		Unit 5: Holiday hot spots	Evaluation	66–69
6b	Using a calculator			
7	**Assess and review**			
8	Shape and space: reasoning about shapes: measures	Unit 4: Spiral paths	Creative thinking	60–63
9	Measures	Unit 2: Mood graphs	Reasoning	36–39
		Unit 3: Giant feet	Enquiry	50–53
		Unit 5: Birdwatching	Evaluation	70–73
10	Shape and Space; Position, movement and scales, and solve problems	Unit 4: Spiral paths	Creative thinking	60–63
11	Addition and subtraction, problems and checking solutions	Unit 1: Cake stall	Information processing	30–33
		Unit 3: The birthday present	Enquiry	46–49
		Unit 3: Giant feet	Enquiry	50–53
		Unit 5: Holiday hot spots	Evaluation	66–69
		Unit 5: Birdwatching	Evaluation	70–73
		Unit 6: Day trip to the beach	Using and applying	80–83
12	Number sequences	Unit 3: The birthday present	Enquiry	46–49
		Unit 4: Washing machines	Creative thinking	56–59
		Unit 6: Discs	Using and applying	76–79
		Unit 6: Radio waves	Using and applying	84–87
13	**Assess and review**			

Spring Term				
		Thinking by Numbers		
Unit	**Unit topic**	**Activity name**	**Thinking skill**	**Page no.**
1	Place value	Unit 3: Giant feet	Enquiry	50–53
2	Multiplication and division 1	Unit 3: The birthday present	Enquiry	46–49
		Unit 4: Washing machines	Creative thinking	56–59
		Unit 4: Spiral paths	Creative thinking	60–63
		Unit 5: Holiday hot spots	Evaluation	66–69
		Unit 5: Birdwatching	Evaluation	70–73
		Unit 6: Daytrip to the beach	Using and applying	80–83
		Unit 6: Radio waves	Using and applying	84–87
3	Multiplication and division 2	Unit 3: The birthday present	Enquiry	46–49
		Unit 3: Giant feet	Enquiry	50–53
		Unit 5: Holiday hot spots	Evaluation	66–69
		Unit 5: Birdwatching	Evaluation	70–73
		Unit 6: Daytrip to the beach	Using and applying	80–83
4	Problem solving	Unit 1: Cake stall	Information processing	30–33
		Unit 3: The birthday present	Enquiry	46–49
		Unit 3: Giant feet	Enquiry	50–53
		Unit 5: Holiday hot spots	Evaluation	66–69
		Unit 5: Birdwatching	Evaluation	70–73
		Unit 6: Day trip to the beach	Using and applying	80–83
5a	Fractions, decimals and percentages	Unit 3: Giant feet	Enquiry	50–53
		Unit 5: Holiday hot spots	Evaluation	66–69
5b	Rotations and reflections			
6	**Assess and review**			
7	Addition and subtraction	Unit 1: Cake stall	Information processing	30–33
		Unit 2: Crossing the river	Reasoning	40–43
		Unit 3: The birthday present	Enquiry	46–49
		Unit 4: Washing machines	Creative thinking	56–59
		Unit 4: Spiral paths	Creative thinking	60–63
		Unit 5: Birdwatching	Evaluation	70–73
		Unit 6: Discs	Using and applying	76–79
		Unit 6: Radio waves	Using and applying	84–87
8	Angles, 2D and 3D shapes, perimeter and area	Unit 3: Giant feet	Enquiry	50–53
		Unit 4: Spiral paths	Creative thinking	60–63
9	Measures and problem solving	Unit 1: Cake stall	Information processing	30–33
		Unit 3: Giant feet	Enquiry	50–53
		Unit 5: Birdwatching	Evaluation	70–73
10	Ratio, proportion, data handling and problem solving	Unit 1: Cake stall	Information processing	30–33
		Unit 5: Holiday hot spots	Evaluation	66–69
11	Properties of reasoning and numbers	Unit 1: The matrix	Information processing	26–29
		Unit 4: Washing machines	Creative thinking	56–59
		Unit 6: Discs	Using and applying	76–79
		Unit 6: Radio waves	Using and applying	84–87
12	**Assess and review**			

Summer Term

Unit	Unit topic	Thinking by Numbers		
		Activity name	Thinking skill	Page no.
1	Decimals, fractions, percentages	Unit 3: Giant feet Unit 5: Holiday hot spots	Enquiry Evaluation	50–53 66–69
2	Calculations	Unit 1: Cake stall Unit 2: Crossing the river Unit 3: The birthday present Unit 4: Washing machines Unit 4: Spiral paths Unit 5: Holiday hot spots Unit 5: Birdwatching Unit 6: Discs Unit 6: Radio waves	Information processing Reasoning Enquiry Creative thinking Creative thinking Evaluation Evaluation Using and applying Using and applying	30–33 40–43 46–49 56–59 60–63 66–69 70–73 76–79 84–87
3	Shape and space	Unit 4: Spiral paths	Creative thinking	60–63
4	Problem solving 1	Unit 1: Cake stall Unit 5: Holiday hot spots	Information processing Evaluation	30–33 66–69
5	Problem solving 2	Unit 1: Cake stall Unit 3: Giant feet Unit 5: Birdwatching	Information processing Enquiry Evaluation	30–33 50–53 70–73
6	Division, decimals, and problem solving	Unit 3: The birthday present Unit 5: Birdwatching	Enquiry Evaluation	46–49 70–73
7	Perimeter, area, calculation and problem solving	Unit 1: Cake stall Unit 3: Giant feet Unit 5: Birdwatching	Information processing Enquiry Evaluation	30–33 50–53 70–73
8	Calculation, percentage, ratio and problem solving	Unit 3: Giant feet Unit 5: Holiday hot spots	Enquiry Evaluation	50–53 66–69
9	Calculation and problem solving	Unit 1: Cake stall Unit 3: The birthday present Unit 3: Giant feet Unit 5: Holiday hot spots Unit 5: Birdwatching Unit 6: Day trip to the beach	Information processing Enquiry Enquiry Evaluation Evaluation Using and applying	30–33 46–49 50–53 66–69 70–73 80–83
10	Fractions, proportion, ratio and problem solving	Unit 3: Giant feet Unit 5: Holiday hot spots	Enquiry Evaluation	50–53 66–69
11	Angles, graphs and problem solving	Unit 4: Spiral paths	Creative thinking	60–63
12	**Assess and review**			

Thinking by Numbers 6 and the NNS Framework

Unit	Thinking skill	Activity name	Place value, ordering and rounding	Properties of numbers and number sequences	Fractions, decimals and percentages, ratio and proportion	Rapid recall of addition and subtraction facts	Mental calculation strategies (+ and −)	Paper and pencil procedures (+ and −)	Understanding multiplication and division	Rapid recall of multiplication and division facts	Mental calculation strategies (× and ÷)	Paper and pencil procedures (× and ÷)	Using a calculator	Checking results of calculations	Making decisions	Reasoning and generalising about numbers or shapes	Problems involving 'real life', money or measures	Measures	Shape and space	Handling data
1	Information processing	The matrix		✓												✓				
1	Information processing	Cake stall				✓	✓							✓			✓	✓		✓
2	Reasoning	Mood graphs																✓		✓
2	Reasoning	Crossing the river				✓	✓							✓		✓				
3	Enquiry	The birthday present		✓		✓	✓	✓	✓	✓	✓	✓		✓	✓		✓			
3	Enquiry	Giant feet	✓		✓	✓	✓	✓				✓			✓		✓	✓		
4	Creative thinking	Washing machines		✓		✓	✓			✓	✓									
4	Creative thinking	Spiral paths				✓				✓	✓			✓		✓			✓	
5	Evaluation	Holiday hot spots			✓	✓	✓	✓	✓	✓	✓	✓			✓	✓	✓	✓		
5	Evaluation	Birdwatching				✓	✓	✓			✓	✓		✓			✓			✓
6	Using and applying thinking skills	Discs		✓			✓									✓				
6	Using and applying thinking skills	Day trip to the beach		✓			✓	✓			✓	✓			✓		✓	✓		
6	Using and applying thinking skills	Radio waves				✓	✓			✓	✓					✓				

Thinking by Numbers 6 and the 5–14 Guidelines

Thinking skill	Unit	Activity name	Problem solving and Enquiry	Information Handling	Range and Type of Numbers	Money	Add and Subtract	Multiply and Divide	Round Numbers	Fractions, Percentages and Ratio	Patterns and Sequences	Functions and Equations	Measure and Estimate	Time	Perimeter, Formulae and Scales	Shape, Position and Movement
Information processing	1	The matrix			✓											
		Cake stall	✓	✓		✓	✓							✓		
Reasoning	2	Mood graphs		✓										✓		
		Crossing the river	✓		✓	✓	✓	✓			✓	✓			✓	
Enquiry	3	The birthday present	✓		✓		✓	✓								
		Giant feet	✓				✓	✓		✓			✓		✓	
Creative thinking	4	Washing machines	✓		✓		✓	✓			✓	✓				
		Spiral paths	✓				✓	✓								✓
Evaluation	5	Holiday hot spots	✓				✓	✓		✓			✓			
		Birdwatching	✓	✓			✓						✓	✓		
Using and applying thinking skills	6	Discs	✓		✓	✓	✓						✓			
		Day trip to the beach	✓				✓	✓			✓	✓		✓		
		Radio waves	✓		✓		✓	✓			✓	✓				

Glossary

algorithm a step by step procedure that, if followed exactly, will always yield a correct solution to a type of problem

assessment for learning an approach to **formative assessment** where the learner is encouraged to take responsibility for evaluating their own achievement of learning objectives. An aspect of **self-regulation**.

Bloom's Taxonomy a widely used instructional objectives model developed by the prominent educator Benjamin Bloom and colleagues in the 1950s. It categorizes the cognitive, affective and conative domains and includes a systematic list of thinking skills, in categories and sub-categories such as comprehension, application, analysis, synthesis, and evaluation. The last three are considered **higher-order** thinking skills.

brain-based learning a range of techniques and approaches to teaching and learning which take their inspiration from research into how the brain works to identify implications for teaching

brainstorm a technique for rapid production of ideas without critical examination, evaluation or elaboration

bridging a teaching strategy where explicit links are drawn from what has been learned to other related contexts to help **transfer**

cognition the mental operations involved in thinking; the biological/neurological processes of the brain that facilitate thought. Sometimes contrasted with affect or emotion and conation (wanting or willing).

Community of Enquiry the process of developing knowledge and understanding by participating in purposeful dialogue or collaborative discussion. Also the teaching technique used in Philosophy for Children with a class of pupils.

concrete preparation an introductory phase in some teaching thinking approaches where new words are introduced and learners become familiar with what the task is about

constructivism a view of learning in which learners are seen as building or developing their own understanding of how the world works from their experience and interaction with people around them

creative thinking producing new ideas or thoughts. Imaginative thinking that is aimed at producing outcomes that involve synthesis of ideas or lateral thinking; thinking that is not analytical or deductive, sometimes referred to as divergent thinking.

critical thinking a generic term for thinking skills used in the United States. The process of determining the authenticity, accuracy, or value of something; characterized by the ability to seek reasons and alternatives, perceive the complete situation, and change one's view based on evidence and reasoning. Sometimes also called analytical or convergent thinking. Often related to formal or informal logic and to reasoning.

demonstrating showing children how to do something, how to perform a skill or a technique, how to carry out a process, how to repeat and practise what they have been shown

dialogue shared enquiry between two or more people

enquiry a systematic or scientific process for answering questions and solving problems based on gathering evidence through observation, analysis and reflection

enquiry learning a teaching strategy designed to develop pupils learning through systematic gathering of observation and investigation

enrichment an approach to teaching thinking as separate discrete skills, usually as separate lessons using a particular programme or set of activities

formative assessment assessment which alters subsequent teaching and learning. This may involve teachers in using information gathered in lessons to alter what they do (see **mediation**) or it may also involve the learner through **assessment for learning**.

graphic organizers diagrams which help learners to organize information such as by comparing and contrasting using a grid of similarities and differences

heuristics general or widely applicable problem-solving strategies. Guidelines that generally direct attention, but that do not always produce a correct outcome (see **algorithm**).

higher order thinking evaluation, synthesis and analysis, the higher levels of **Bloom's Taxonomy**

infusion integrating thinking skills teaching into the regular curriculum or lessons; infused programs are commonly contrasted with **enrichment** programs, where separate or discrete skills are taught through lessons to promote thinking.

mediation a teaching strategy where the teacher intervenes and supports the development of pupils' understanding by **modelling** or by direct instruction to help them achieve something they could not do alone

metacognition the process of planning, assessing, and monitoring one's own thinking. Thinking about thinking in order to develop understanding or **self-regulation**.

modelling teaching children in a way that helps them to see the underlying structures, and to understand the embedded or supporting concepts and ideas

multiple intelligences the idea developed by Howard Gardner that IQ does not measure aspects of intelligence sufficiently and that people have strengths in different areas such as visual-spatial or musical as well as more traditionally assessed areas such as linguistic or logico-mathematical

problem based learning an approach using **problem solving** techniques where learners are set specific challenges through realistic or unstructured problems. Similar to **enquiry learning**, but with a particular goal or challenge which needs to be resolved

problem solving a general term which covers a diversity of problem types which make a range of demands on thinking. Some problems have unique solutions and can be tackled with predominantly convergent critical thinking, but many others are open-ended and demand both creative and critical thinking for their solution.

reasoning drawing conclusions or inferences from observations, facts, experiences: deductive inferring conclusions from premises; inductive: inferring a provisional conclusion or hypothesis from information

self-regulation the conscious use of mental strategies to improve thinking and learning, often aimed at particular learning goals

seriation sequencing or arranging objects, ideas or events in a particular order determined by a criterion

Socratic questioning an approach to questioning and discussion where answers to questions are pursued through dialogue

thinking skills 'thinking skills' and related terms are used to indicate a teaching approach which emphasizes the processes of thinking and learning that can be used in a range of contexts. The list of thinking skills in the English National Curriculum is similar to many such lists: information-processing, reasoning, enquiry, creative thinking and evaluation.

transfer the ability to apply an idea or a skill that has been learnt in one context and use it in a different context